FARADAY, MAXWELL, AND KELVIN

Born in Glasgow, Scotland, in 1920, DAVID KEITH CHALMERS MACDONALD received his M.A. in mathematics and natural philosophy from Edinburgh University in 1941, and his Ph.D. in 1946 after serving with the Royal Mechanical and Electrical Engineers during World War II. He then went to Oxford as a research fellow. There he continued his graduate studies and took a second Ph.D. (1949).

In 1951 Dr. MacDonald went to Canada to start a laboratory in low temperature and solid state physics for the National Research Council in Ottawa. This low temperature physics research laboratory has become very well known, and has grown from a staff of one—himself—to a group of fifteen scientists.

Dr. MacDonald contributed significantly to our knowledge of the transport properties of metals and alloys. Some of his most important contributions were in the field of electrical resistance at low temperatures. Furthermore, under his guidance the Low Temperature Group did valuable work on specific heats, atomic spacings in crystals, and semiconductor physics.

In 1955 Dr. MacDonald was appointed honorary chairman of the Physics Department at Ottawa University. He helped to launch this department on a program of low temperature physics research. Through his many radio and television broadcasts, he brought science to wider audiences and thereby increased Canadian interest in physics.

Dr. MacDonald was elected a Fellow of the Royal Society of Edinburgh in 1954, a Fellow of the Royal

Society of Canada in 1958, and a Fellow of the Royal Society of London in 1960. In 1960 the Canadian Association of Physicists awarded him its fifth Gold Medal for Achievement in Physics. He was a frequent contributor to scientific journals and the author of another Science Study Series book, *Near Zero: The Physics of Low Temperature*.

Dr. MacDonald died in July of 1963 after a protracted illness.

Faraday, Maxwell, and Kelvin

BY D. K. C. MACDONALD

SCIENCE
STUDY
SERIES

Published by Anchor Books

Doubleday & Company, Inc.

Garden City, New York

1964

Library of Congress Catalog Card Number 64–11313

First Edition

THE SCIENCE STUDY SERIES

The Science Study Series offers to students and to the general public the writing of distinguished authors on the most stirring and fundamental topics of science, from the smallest known particles to the whole universe. Some of the books tell of the role of science in the world of man, his technology and civilization. Others are biographical in nature, telling the fascinating stories of the great discoverers and their discoveries. All the authors have been selected both for expertness in the fields they discuss and for ability to communicate their special knowledge and their own views in an interesting way. The primary purpose of these books is to provide a survey within the grasp of the young student or the layman. Many of the books, it is hoped, will encourage the reader to make his own investigations of natural phenomena.

The Series, which now offers topics in all the sciences and their applications, had its beginning in a project to revise the secondary schools' physics curriculum. At the Massachusetts Institute of Technology during 1956 a group of physicists, high school teachers, journalists, apparatus designers, film producers, and other specialists organized the Physical Science Study Committee, now operating as part of Educational Services Incorporated, Watertown, Massachusetts. They pooled their knowledge and experience toward the design and creation of aids to the learning of physics. Initially their effort was supported by the National Science Foundation, which has continued to aid the program. The Ford Foundation, the Fund for the Advancement of Education, and the Alfred P. Sloan Foundation have also given support. The Committee has created a textbook, an extensive film series, a laboratory guide, especially designed apparatus, and a teacher's source book.

The Series is guided by a Board of Editors consisting of Bruce F. Kingsbury, Managing Editor; John H. Durston, General Editor; Paul F. Brandwein, the Conservation Foundation and Harcourt, Brace & World, Inc.; Samuel A. Goudsmit, Brookhaven National Laboratory; Philippe LeCorbeiller, Harvard University; and Gerard Piel, *Scientific American*.

PREFACE

Today the advertising giants tell us constantly over radio and television about the tremendous strides forward that are made by their products from day to day. Indeed, if we took all advertisements at face value, we would have to believe that epoch-making discoveries were being made hourly in every sort of product from automobiles to face soap.

Personally, I find all this rather tiresome, to say the least, and it may also be quite dangerous, because our young people quickly become very cynical about the whole business, and must then doubt whether anyone *ever* makes really important discoveries. This in turn may play a part in generating boredom with the world around, and I am largely convinced that, of all man's enemies, boredom is the most dangerous. I have found it refreshing to browse through the lives of three very great men—Faraday, Maxwell, and Kelvin, who made truly epoch-making discoveries in their lives. The more I read about men such as these and what they accomplished, the more impressed I become with what a really productive human being can accomplish in a single life.

Recently I read a review of a science biography which suggested that, while the science in the biography was there all right, the picture of the man involved was rather like a cardboard figure. If anyone feels that I have concentrated too much in this short book on personal aspects of my heroes' lives, perhaps they will forgive my desire to try to make something more than cardboard figures of these men.

Authors sometimes mention that this and that will be their best reward; apart from my natural hope that this book will be bought, read, and perhaps even enjoyed, my best reward would be if it also should arouse sufficient interest in readers to make them wish to read fuller and more authoritative accounts about Faraday, Maxwell, and Kelvin.

D. K. C. MacDonald

Ottawa: December 1962

ACKNOWLEDGMENTS

In putting together biographical sketches such as these it seems impossible to acknowledge fully the debt one owes to all sources of information that one draws on. I hope sincerely that if I have omitted to thank anyone or to acknowledge duly permission granted to reproduce quotations, photographs, letters, etc., I shall be forgiven.

It is a sincere pleasure for me to thank:

My secretary, Mrs. T. F. Armitage, for typing and checking many drafts of the manuscript.

Dr. J. S. Dugdale for help in checking the proofs, etc.

Macmillan & Co., Ltd., publishers, London, for permission to make short quotations from their book *The Life of Lord Kelvin* (two volumes) by Silvanus P. Thompson (1910), and for permission to reproduce a portrait of Lord Kelvin from this book; and for their permission to make short quotations from their book *The Life of James Clerk Maxwell* by L. Campbell and W. Garnett (1882).

Longmans, Green & Co., Ltd., publishers, London, for confirming that I would be free to make quotations from their book *The Life and Letters of Faraday* (two volumes) by Bence Jones (1870).

The Royal Society of Edinburgh; the Royal Society of London; the University of Glasgow; the University of Aberdeen; the Cavendish Laboratory in the University of Cambridge; King's College in the University of London; Departments of the University of Edinburgh; the Royal Institution of London; the Dean and Chapter of Westminster Abbey; National Portrait Gallery, London; Society for the Promotion of Christian Knowledge; and United Press International, Ottawa, for their kind permission to reproduce photographs, letters, apparatus, etc., as detailed in the captions throughout the book.

Dr. R. O. Davies; Dr. D. M. Finlayson; Dr. A. D. I. Nicol; Professor J. C. Gunn; Dr. A. F. Brown; Dr. G. Wyllie; Mr. Sam Callander; Professor C. Domb; Dr. C. S. Beals, Dominion Astronomer; Mr. R. J. F. Carnon; and Miss Helen Revie, for their personal kindness in obtaining photographic reproductions of letters, instruments, etc., as detailed in the captions or in the text.

Many people, such as Professor A. B. Pippard; Sir Harold Hartley; Sir George Thomson; Sir Patrick Linstead; Dr. R. Schlapp; Mr. B. A. Stenhouse; and Professor K. G. Emeleus, for so kindly answering my letters with queries of one kind and another; and many other people, such as the library staff of the National Research Council for looking up, and finding, answers to my questions.

Finally, my father, Mr. George MacDonald, for his most valuable help.

PLATES 1 AND 12:   By kind permission of the National Portrait Gallery, London.

PLATE 2:   From a water color drawing by T. H. Shepherd, and reproduced by kind permission of the Royal Institution.

PLATE 3:   Photograph by R. B. Fleming & Co., Ltd., London, and reproduced by kind permission of the Royal Society of London.

PLATES 4, 9, AND 10:   By kind permission of the Royal Institution, London.

PLATE 6:   By kind permission of the Royal Society of London.

PLATES 7 AND 8:   Photographs by John R. Freeman & Co., Ltd., London, and reproduced by kind permission of the Royal Society of London.

PLATE 13:   I am most grateful to Dr. R. O. Davies for his kindness in obtaining for me this photograph, taken by

R. B. Fleming & Co., Ltd., London. The photograph is reproduced by kind permission of the Institution of Electrical Engineers in London.

PLATE 14: Reproduced by kind permission of the Society for the Propagation of Christian Knowledge.

PLATE 15: I am very grateful to my father, Mr. George MacDonald, for supplying these photographs taken by J. Campbell Harper, Ltd., Edinburgh.

PLATE 16: I am most grateful to my father, Mr. George MacDonald, for this photograph, and also for photographs of the memorial inside Corsock Church, all of which he took.

PLATES 17 AND 18a: I am most grateful to Mr. Sam Callander, Registrar for the Corsock district, for letting me have these photographs which he took.

PLATES 18b AND 18c: Photographs taken by Mr. George MacDonald.

PLATE 19: I am grateful to Professor C. Domb, King's College, London, for supplying me with the copy of this postcard, which is reproduced by kind permission of King's College, University of London.

PLATE 20: By kind permission of the University of Aberdeen.

PLATES 21, 25, AND 42: Reproduced by kind permission of the Royal Society of Edinburgh.

PLATE 22: Reproduced through the courtesy of Edinburgh University Library.

PLATE 23: I am most grateful to Dr. A. F. Brown, University of Edinburgh, for obtaining this photograph for me, which is reproduced by kind permission of the Medical Photography Unit, University of Edinburgh.

PLATE 24: I am grateful to Dr. C. S. Beals, F.R.S., Dominion Astronomer, for letting me have for reproduction this "Lick Observatory Photograph."

PLATES 26, 27, 28, 29, 30, 31, 32, 38, AND 39: Reproduced by kind permission from the Cavendish Laboratory, Cambridge.

PLATE 33: I am most grateful to Messrs. Macmillan & Co., Ltd., London, for giving me permission to reproduce this photogravure by Emery Walker from their book *Life of Lord Kelvin* by Silvanus P. Thompson.

PLATE 34: I am very grateful to my cousin, Miss Helen Revie, for giving me these photographs, both of which she took.

PLATES 35, 36, 37, AND 45: Reproduced by kind permission of the University of Glasgow.

PLATE 40: I am very grateful to Dr. G. Wyllie, F.R.S.E., for letting me have a photographic copy of this letter which is reproduced by kind permission of the University of Glasgow.

PLATE 41: Professor J. C. Gunn, F.R.S.E., very kindly supplied this photograph, and tells me that it shows the University buildings as they were in 1890 and that the Natural Philosophy classroom in which Kelvin lectured is on the left of the tower as we look at the photograph. By kind permission of the University of Glasgow.

PLATES 43 AND 44: I am very grateful to Dr. R. O. Davies for his kindness in obtaining for me these photographs. Photographs taken by George Miles Ltd., London, and reproduced by kind permission of the Dean and Chapter of Westminster Abbey.

CONTENTS

Chapter I

INTRODUCTION

"History is bunk"; or so, I am told, said Henry Ford. And George Sarton (1884–1956), a great Harvard scholar, said that: "The history of science is the only history which can illustrate the progress of mankind." Whether Ford or Sarton be right or not, it does seem to me that at school I had to learn much about the doings of Kings, Queens, Good and Bad Barons, and innumerable Generals, whereas many of these supposedly distinguished people had really much less influence on our lives than some of the great scientists of the past have had. Now to this very day, at the age of forty-two, I still cannot keep quite straight who reigned in Britain (where I was born), and when and why *before* Queen Victoria. Chiefly because postage stamps, in which as a boy I was very interested, were first issued in 1840 (in Britain, of course!), I have always had very clearly in mind that Queen Victoria reigned from 1837 to 1901, and I have tended to regard her as being a person of very great influence on our lives—always assuming one had the good sense to be born and bred in the British Commonwealth (and in case anyone is in doubt, this remark is really not meant to be taken too seriously!). But it has been said before, and I think it may be true, that the discoveries of Michael Faraday, who lived at much the same time as Queen Victoria, have had a far greater influence on our lives than anything the Widow of Windsor[1] ever did.

In a rather similar vein I have fixed indelibly in my mind also that the Plague swept over London, England, in 1665, and that the Great Fire of London occurred the following year, 1666. It appeared to me as a boy that the *major* consequence of these events was that Sir Christopher Wren[2] designed St. Paul's Cathedral in London. Now St. Paul's is certainly a fine building, and the remaking of London was most important, but a vital consequence for mankind as a whole was that the threat of the Plague in 1664 caused Cambridge University students to leave the University and return to their homes for a period. One of these students was Isaac Newton, who went back to his country birthplace in Woolsthorpe for about eighteen months, and produced there some of the finest scientific work the world has ever known.

What I am trying to argue is that if we *should* know something about wars and conquests, and about the Rulers and Generals who made them, then whether we intend to be physicians, explorers, business executives, or just plain ordinary folk, we *also* ought to know something about the men who laid the scientific foundations for a great part of our modern civilization. Now one of my colleagues suggests to me that any idea of history as primarily recording the dates of battles, victories, and defeats, etc., is long since outmoded, so perhaps I am just "knocking at an open door," or "flogging a dead horse," whichever metaphor you prefer. My reply is that this is how it was when I was at school, and my younger daughter in grade ten in high school today suggests to me that it has not changed very much since. Right or wrong, this is my official apology for attempting to write this little book about three very great British scientists, Faraday, Maxwell, and Kelvin, who all lived in the last century. The nineteenth century was a most remarkable one for British science, and I have found the lives of these three outstanding contributors, Faraday, Maxwell, and Kelvin, rather fascinating. Moreover, two of these three men were of Scots blood, which provided an added reason for me to try to write this book.

Michael Faraday was born in 1791, William Thomson (later Lord Kelvin) died in 1907, and their lives thus spanned a period of enormous change in Europe. The Industrial Revolution in Great Britain was just beginning when Faraday was a boy: perhaps the movement of his parents from Yorkshire to London two or three before his birth was part of the general trend toward the cities. The technical use of electricity was unknown when Faraday was born, but by the time of Lord Kelvin's death an enormous electrical industry of all kinds had sprung up, and indeed Kelvin himself played a considerable part in this very growth. The social origins of Faraday, Maxwell, and Kelvin were all quite different, and illustrate well that science is a career or vocation where wealth or social standing is of no consequence in achieving the highest positions or honors, but only intellectual eminence counts.

Faraday's father was a blacksmith,* William Thomson was the son of a mathematics teacher of rather limited means, while James Clerk Maxwell came from a well-to-do Scottish family which I suppose one might describe as part of the "landed gentry." Maxwell's uncle was in fact an hereditary baronet (Sir George Clerk, Bt., of Penicuik), and so between Faraday's family and Maxwell's family there would have been

---

* Perhaps I should mention that a blacksmith was to a horse what a good mechanic is today to an automobile. A blacksmith's main task those days was the shoeing of horses at his smithy. While this was of course a perfectly honorable job, the *status* of a blacksmith was pretty humble in eighteenth and nineteenth century England.

quite a large social gulf, and I suppose you could say that they belonged to the opposite sides of the railway tracks. Yet this disparity in social background had no influence whatsoever on the respect they had for one another's work or on their scientific correspondence. Indeed by the luck of the draw, and also because he did not live long enough, Maxwell himself never seems to have been in the running to have a title conferred on him, and he received but two honorary degrees from British universities, while on the other hand Faraday and Kelvin both had literally scores of honors of one kind and another showered on them because of their work. However, I suppose the finest honor of all, could Maxwell have lived to know it, is that "Maxwell's equations" describing electromagnetic phenomena under all sorts of possible conditions, remain basically just as true and vital today as when Maxwell himself proposed them.† The discovery of these laws by Maxwell is regarded by physicists all over the world as the same kind of gigantic achievement as was Newton's discovery of his equations of motion. If one tries to assess Faraday, Maxwell, and Kelvin in some sort of order of greatness, then there is little doubt that Max-

---

† Reported scientific discoveries of one kind and another may prove later to be incorrect because experiments were inaccurate or theories inadequate, and so what seemed important at one time may be forgotten in later years. Alternatively, and perhaps more sadly, some discovery may remain quite true, but come to be regarded later as rather trivial.

A story about the great Swiss theoretical physicist Wolfgang Pauli, who died recently (December 1958), bears repetition. A colleague sent him some work by a young man in order to have Pauli's opinion. The colleague himself was somewhat dubious about the merit of the work, and one might say that Pauli himself did not tolerate fools gladly. After a few days, when Pauli was asked about the work, he shook his head (a most characteristic gesture), saying, "It wasn't even wrong!"

well would come first, but this is in no way to diminish the achievements of Faraday and Kelvin; it is only to recognize that probably the three most remarkable physical scientists since the time of Galileo have been Isaac Newton, James Clerk Maxwell, and Albert Einstein.

Mark you, by no means everyone, and not even those in the universities, seemed aware of the greatness of Maxwell's work during his life. Maxwell[3] himself told the following incident to Sir J. J. Thomson, who told it to Sir Edward Appleton, who told it to T. A. F. Noble, who is now the Principal of Leicester University. It seems that the Vice-Chancellor of Cambridge University was introducing Maxwell to a Cambridge audience and spoke as follows: "Ladies and Gentlemen, you can have no idea how difficult it has been to get a suitable speaker for this occasion. We tried first one and then another and one after the other declined the invitation. We were in despair, but luckily at last Professor Clerk Maxwell agreed to accept our invitation. We are very fortunate indeed to have Professor Clerk Maxwell here as our speaker . . ." Perhaps physicists can never hope to achieve the renown of baseball players, or hockey stars in Canada, but surely Maxwell deserved more gallant treatment than this—and at the University where he was a professor!

I have complained at times that chairmen at lectures and banquets spend far too long *introducing* people, so let us forthwith get down to brass tacks.

NOTES

1. Windsor Castle is a traditional home of the British monarchy. When Queen Victoria's husband, Prince Albert, died, she was inconsolable and observed mourning

for very many years, so earning the title of the Widow of Windsor.

2. "Sir Christopher Wren
   Went to dine with some men.
   He said, 'If anyone calls,
   Tell them I'm designing St. Paul's.'"
   —E. Clerihew Bentley, 1875

Wren was not only an architect but a distinguished scientist of his day, and he and Edmund Halley, the astronomer (remember "Halley's Comet"), played an important part in ultimately persuading Isaac Newton to write his famous *Principia* dealing with the foundations of mechanics and physics.

3. Maxwell himself was the first professor in charge of the famous Cavendish Laboratory at Cambridge University. When he died he was succeeded by Lord Rayleigh, whose investigations on acoustics, and vibrations in general, remain unsurpassed today. Rayleigh in turn was succeeded by J. J. Thomson, who was later knighted and to whom is credited the experimental discovery of the electron in 1897. J. J. Thomson, who incidentally was no relation to William Thomson (Lord Kelvin), attracted Ernest Rutherford to Cambridge, and Rutherford (later Sir Ernest Rutherford and finally Lord Rutherford) brought tremendous luster to the Cavendish Laboratory by his famous experiments on the structure of the atomic nucleus. Rutherford was succeeded in 1938 as head of the Cavendish Laboratory by Sir Lawrence Bragg, who shared the 1915 Nobel Prize jointly with his father, W. H. Bragg, for their remarkable pioneer work on the X-ray analysis of crystals. Sir Lawrence Bragg is now Resident Professor and Director of the Royal Institution in London, which was originally headed by Sir Humphry Davy and in turn by Michael Faraday himself. The present successor to Sir Lawrence Bragg in Cambridge is Sir Nevill Mott, who is probably best known today for his outstanding theoretical investigations on metals.

Sir Edward Appleton, who is now Principal and Vice-Chancellor of Edinburgh University, worked at the Cavendish Laboratory for some years after the First World War, and won renown for his experimental researches on the reflection of radio waves from the ionosphere. Indeed, one of the principal reflecting layers in the ionosphere is named after Appleton; the other is known as the Heaviside layer, after the English physicist Oliver Heaviside (1850–1925).

Chapter II

MICHAEL FARADAY

EARLY LIFE

Michael Faraday (Plates 1 and 12) came of a Yorkshire family, but his father, James Faraday, the blacksmith, had moved to the County of Surrey, close to London, before the birth of Michael. Michael Faraday was born September 22, 1791, at a place called Newington Butts; "Butts" refers to land used for firing practice, and Newington Butts was originally reserved for archery practice. Although in those days it was a country village, the place is now looked on as only a stone's throw from Waterloo Station, which we should now regard as almost in the heart of London. This move of James Faraday and his family from Yorkshire to the London region was presumably a consequence of the Industrial Revolution, which in Britain extended roughly from the middle of the eighteenth century to the middle of the nineteenth century and resulted in a considerable move of rural populations to the great cities where work was now more plentiful. Other countries, of course, had their industrial revolutions, but these occurred rather later than in Britain; the main transformation of the United States to industrialization took place after the middle of the last century, while in Canada one might say that its industrial revolution is really in full swing today.

Economically speaking, the Faraday family must have been in a very modest state; Dr. Bence Jones,

Faraday's biographer,* says that in 1801 when food was extremely expensive Michael, then nine years old, could have only one loaf a week as an allowance of bread.

Two features of Faraday's early life stand out very clearly: that he was brought up in rather basic, simple, early Christian principles, to which he tried to remain faithful throughout his life; secondly, that his early education and training were of only a rather elementary character. The Faraday family all belonged to a somewhat obscure religious sect known as the Sandemanians. Robert Sandeman was the son-in-law, and follower, of one John Glas (1695–1773), who founded an independent Presbyterian group when he was deposed on theological grounds from the main Presbyterian church in Scotland. Glas and Sandeman argued that national, or "established," churches would always conflict with the basic principles of Christianity and, to quote Bence Jones: ". . . that the Bible, and that alone, with nothing added to it nor taken away from it by man, was the sole and sufficient guide for each individual, at all times and in all circumstances; . . ." It appears that Faraday during his life remained very loyal to the Sandemanian ideas, even when he had achieved the great fame which became his in later years. I have read that Faraday in his later years was introduced to a high dignitary of the Church of England, who asked him, perhaps somewhat patronizingly, if he really believed that the Sandemanians had a monopoly on religious truth; to this Faraday replied cheerfully that he felt this not at all, but that their faith was also quite capable of leading them to heaven. Presumably the scriptural

* We are referring to *The Life and Letters of Faraday* by Dr. Bence Jones, published by Longmans, Green & Co., Ltd., London, in 1870. Subsequent quotations from the letters, etc., of Faraday himself are as reported in Bence Jones' biography.

advice "to take no thought for the morrow," interpreted strictly, was what led Faraday never to take out any life insurance, despite the fact that his affection and concern for his wife are clearly shown in his letters.

Of his early education Faraday tells us himself: "My education was of the most ordinary description, consisting of little more than the rudiments of reading, writing, and arithmetic at a common day-school. My hours out of school were passed at home and in the streets." Remarks such as these lend support to Bence Jones' assessment of Faraday: "This leaves no doubt that Faraday rose from that large class which lives by the hardest muscular labour, and can give but little for mental food; . . ." When Faraday was about twelve he went to work, at first as an errand boy, at a bookseller's store owned by a Mr. George Riebau. It was part of Faraday's job "to carry around papers that were lent out by his master." Once again this suggests clearly that in the England of those days Faraday's lot was a rather humble one, since some class distinction has always tended to be applied there to jobs such as errand-boy or paper-boy. I have often felt that the situation in North America in this respect is a refreshing contrast, where one feels that to have had a paper route as a boy is an almost essential step to becoming President of the United States or perhaps even Prime Minister of Canada.

As a bookbinder's assistant Faraday had the opportunity, which might otherwise not have come his way, of seeing and reading scientific books of one kind or another. When Faraday was about nineteen, a Mr. Dance, who was visiting the bookseller's shop, gave him tickets to attend a series of lectures to be given in London by Sir Humphry Davy. If ever there was a vital turning point in a man's life, then certainly these lectures which he attended were just that for Faraday.

Humphry Davy was the brilliant Professor of Chemistry at the Royal Institution in London, and Faraday's whole scientific career was bound up with the Royal Institution. And what was, or is, the Royal Institution?

COUNT RUMFORD AND THE ROYAL INSTITUTION

To answer this question we must go back to a very remarkable man, Benjamin Thompson, who was born in Woburn, Massachusetts, in 1753. Benjamin Thompson was not, it seems, in favor of the patriot cause in the American Revolution, and so he went to England in 1776. He was very interested in science, and in 1779 was elected to the Royal Society of London, about which more later. Thompson served with the English military forces in America, became a colonel, and was ultimately knighted, so becoming Sir Benjamin Thompson. Perhaps he became bored with the peaceful life when the War of Independence was over, for in 1784 he went to Bavaria to work as a soldier and minister of the state there. He was ultimately made a Count of the Holy Roman Empire for his services to the Kingdom of Bavaria, and chose the title of Count Rumford.[1] This name he took from the town of Rumford in New Hampshire, which later was renamed Concord. Rumford was concerned with problems of making military guns, and experiments which he made on the relationship of friction and heat, arising from the boring out of cannon barrels in the arsenal at Munich in Bavaria, constitute great pioneer contributions to science.

Before Rumford's time, and indeed for many years after it, there was much discussion by physicists and chemists about the fundamental nature of heat. For a time it was believed that heat was itself some kind of separate substance (known as "caloric"), which when added to bodies made them hot. Rumford, in a beautiful paper published in the Transactions of the Royal Society in 1798, drew the conclusion that in the last analysis heat must be nothing but a motion of individual particles of matter (or the random motion of atoms or molecules, as we should say today). However, despite the clarity of Rumford's paper, even so great a scientist as William Thomson (Lord Kelvin) appeared to adhere to the "caloric" theory until around the middle of the nineteenth century. It was the experiments of James Prescott Joule that finally convinced Kelvin of the fact that heat was just a form of energy. This concept of the nature of heat can be called the "kinetic theory of heat."

We are told that Rumford did an excellent job in Bavaria in arranging programs of useful work to cut down the numbers of troublesome vagabonds, and this interest in solving social problems must have persisted with him. Sanborn Brown, in his study of Rumford (*Count Rumford,* Doubleday & Co., Inc., 1962) says of Rumford: "He himself initiated many of our modern improvements in day-to-day living. As a sociologist, he initiated extremely advanced experiments in organizing people to understand and make use of new information." On the other hand, Sanborn Brown suggests that Rumford was not a particularly attractive person in himself: "He was not really interested in people and their human problems. He tried to use people rather than to help them," and Brown even says: "People who tried to live and to work with [Rumford] found it so difficult to give him credit for his real achievements that when his life was over they just forgot him as fast as possible."

Rumford went to London again in 1798 from Bavaria and became associated with the Society for Bettering the Condition and Increasing the Comforts of the Poor. He was then led to propose: ". . . for forming by subscription, in the Metropolis of the British Empire, a *Public Institution* for diffusing the knowledge and facilitating the general introduction of useful mechanical inventions and improvements, and for teaching by courses of philosophical lectures and experiments the application of science to the common purposes of life"; and on March 7, 1799, the so-called *Royal Institution of Great Britain* was founded (Plate 2).

The founding meeting of the Royal Institution was presided over by Sir Joseph Banks (a president of the Royal Society of London), who turns up again later in the story when Faraday first sought scientific employment. The Royal Institution's original concern for improving the conditions of the poorer classes in particular soon ceased to be of primary interest, and the body became and remained essentially a scientific institute where research could be carried out and courses of lectures given. If one asks further about the unique significance and achievements of the Royal Institution, we can turn to its General Secretary from 1929–50, who said: ". . . a simple answer, and of far greater significance to many people, is that it is the place where Faraday lived and worked. The 'promotion of science' may mean much or little, and there are other societies with similar objects, but there has been only one Michael Faraday." (T. Martin, *The Royal Institution,* 3rd ed., The Royal Institution, 1961)

Count Rumford persuaded Humphry Davy (Plate 3), who was a very brilliant young chemist hailing originally from Cornwall, to join the Royal Institution in 1801 as assistant lecturer in chemistry and director of the laboratory. Very shortly thereafter he was appointed lecturer, and was promoted to professor on May 31, 1802. Davy was only twenty-three years old when he took up this senior appointment. We sometimes like to think that in the bad old days men always had to work very hard and long to gain some recognition in contrast to our modern, "enlightened" and "democratic" world, but our ancestors were hardly backward in recognizing genius when they appointed, at one place or another, Isaac Newton, Humphry Davy, Clerk Maxwell, and William Thomson to full professorships, all by the age of twenty-five. Apart from research in chemistry, part of Davy's work at the Royal Institution was to give lectures, or "Discourses" as they are known, and it was to a course of these lectures that Michael Faraday received an invitation from Mr. Dance, the customer who visited Riebau's bookshop. Davy not only was a brilliant research worker but also, according to his contemporaries, gave exciting lectures. Perhaps Davy is best known (at least he was to *me* as a boy) for his invention of the miner's safety lamp, but it may have been his experiments using electric arcs to achieve very high temperatures which most interested Faraday (see Plate 4).

EARLY INVESTIGATIONS OF ELECTRICITY

Electricity had been known in one form or another for centuries, and men had learned to store relatively small quantities of electricity in what were called Leyden jars, or what we would now today call electrical condensers or capacitors—that is, two pieces of metal or metal foil close to one another but separated by an insulator. When a condenser has been charged with electricity, it may subsequently be discharged by putting a piece of wire across the two metal plates, a fat spark being produced, or else a possibly dangerous electric shock if one should be careless enough to take hold of it. Electrical condensers are still enormously important today; for example, one can produce very large bursts of current for a brief time by charging up a bank of condensers slowly (over several minutes perhaps), and then discharging the condensers in a fraction of a second. Such short-lived, but very large, electric currents can be used to produce very large magnetic fields for various experimental purposes, but apparatus to record what happens in so brief a time becomes complicated. Further, the condenser can supply only the net amount of electric charge one has put in, and in Davy's time it was often quite a long-winded process to charge up condensers, whose discharge might be complete in an instant.

What was very badly needed, both for a host of practical purposes and to enable research into electricity to go ahead, was some device that could produce a *steady* flow of electric current lasting for a goodly period of time. This is a typical situation in the development of any new physical principle or discovery. For example, in the early days of gas liquefaction a small apparatus might be made which would ultimately produce a few transient drops of liquid oxygen which then immediately boiled away. This stage in the work of discovery is vital because it proves that the thing "can be done," but, as someone later remarked, one could not be satisfied with the technique until one had a liter or so of liquid oxygen boiling quietly in a retort. It is true that very important scientific experiments which uncover some new principle often have been made with makeshift equipment and "string and sealing-wax" apparatus, and Helmholtz said of Faraday himself that "a few wires and some old bits of wood and iron seem to serve him for the greatest discoveries." But it may also require yet another type of far-reaching mind to see how the often rickety and unreliable apparatus of the original discovery can lead to equipment or devices which will operate reliably and for long periods without attention.

The vital step forward to enable work to be done with a steady source of electricity was taken about 1800 by Alessandro Volta (1745–1827), who made the first "voltaic cells" or batteries. When two different metals are placed in contact, an electric potential difference (called the Volta potential or contact potential) is produced, but an electric current cannot be maintained in this way alone. However, by immersing two different materials (so-called electrodes) in a suitable conducting solution (i.e., an electrolyte), we can make a cell in which a chemical reaction can go on between the electrodes and electrolyte, and cause a steady electric current to be provided from the cell for lengthy periods. Of course, you don't get something for nothing—at least never in the physical world of nature. The energy to provide the flowing electric current comes from the continual chemical change in the electrodes of the cell which goes on steadily so long as you draw an electric current from the cell. Ultimately, if the chemical reaction is allowed to go on unchecked, the cell becomes useless. With certain types of cells, such as those used for car batteries, the chemical reaction is reversible in the sense that, when you have drawn current for some time, you can make the chemical reaction go back the other way and so restore the cell to its original condition, by driving a current through the cell in the opposite direction. This is just what happens when your car battery is re-charged from the car generator (or at a service station if the car generator has stopped working!).

With cells or batteries as a source of electricity we can maintain an intense source of light and heat by setting up a continuous "electric arc" between two rods of carbon. For a great many years such arc lamps

(Plate 5) have been used for theater spotlights, and for film projectors in movies, although they are probably less common today. The temperature produced in such an arc can be very high, and to a chemist such as Humphry Davy this would be very valuable for melting stubborn materials and for accelerating chemical reactions, since it is a quite general principle that chemical reactions will proceed more rapidly the higher the temperature.

FARADAY JOINS THE ROYAL INSTITUTION AS DAVY'S ASSISTANT

Michael Faraday attended some of these lectures by Davy, and tells us in his own words: "During my apprenticeship I had the good fortune, . . . to hear four of the last lectures of Sir H. Davy. . . . Of these I made notes, and then wrote out the lectures in a fuller form, interspersing them with such drawings as I could make. The desire to be engaged in scientific occupation, even though of the lowest kind, induced me, whilst an apprentice, to write, in my ignorance of the world and simplicity of my mind, to Sir Joseph Banks, then President of the Royal Society. Naturally enough," says Faraday, "no answer was the reply left with the porter." Despite this snub, Faraday was not discouraged and later tried a direct approach to Davy himself: "Under the encouragement of Mr. Dance [who was a member of the Royal Institution and had provided the tickets for Davy's lectures], I wrote to Sir Humphry Davy, sending, as a proof of my earnestness, the notes I had taken of his last four lectures. The reply was immediate, kind and favourable." Ultimately, in the early part of 1813, when Faraday was twenty-one years old, Humphry Davy found him employment in the Royal Institution as a laboratory assistant. The Minutes of the Royal

Institution for March 1, 1813, read: "Sir Humphry Davy has the honour to inform the Managers that he has found a person who is desirous to occupy the situation. . . . His name is Michael Faraday. . . . His habits seem good, his disposition active and cheerful, and his manner intelligent."

In October of the same year, after Faraday had just turned twenty-two, he went abroad to Europe with Sir Humphry and Lady Davy. Davy's fame as a scientist had spread throughout Europe, and he was allowed to travel through France despite the fact that in 1813 England was at war with Napoleon. The contrast with life today could hardly be more poignant. If two countries were at war today, probably the *last* people that either nation would allow to travel freely in their countries would be scientists! In recent years, wars have become far more all-enveloping, and people have been taught to hate one another much more effectively. But Davy himself remarked: "If two countries or governments are at war, the men of science are not. . . . That would indeed be a civil war of the worst description. . . ." It seems that in times gone by the people of one nation were not expected to hate those of another nation just because their rulers chose to make war with one another. On the other hand, in those days also I presume rulers or their governments were less involved in the day-to-day affairs or livelihood of their citizens (after all, the hated income tax itself did not even exist in Britain before the Napoleonic Wars!). So while supposedly benevolent and rather gigantic governments are needed today to redistribute the wealth of the country among the citizens and to dispense much needed welfare, unemployment benefits, and so on, perhaps we now pay the enormous penalty that in effect the government makes us "belong" to it, and in the end makes us hate people *en masse* in other countries, whom after all we have never seen nor met, nor are likely so to do.

This tour through Europe, in the course of which Davy met a number of distinguished European scientists, lasted for a full year and a half; the party did not return to England until April 1815, and even at that it seems that the trip was cut somewhat short. Faraday, when writing to his mother, says that he was not sure whether their rather sudden return to England at that time was occasioned by political events in Europe, or (one suspects) at least partly because of personal discord between Sir Humphry Davy and his wife. In fact, Lady Davy seems to have been what is called a rather "difficult" woman in some ways. On April 11, 1812, Humphry Davy had married a Mrs. Apreece, just three days after he had been knighted by the Prince Regent, and his wife, now Lady Davy, accompanied Davy on his extensive visit to the Continent. Mrs. Apreece herself was a wealthy young widow from Scotland. Perhaps the new glamor of her husband's knighthood, and the fact that she was already something of a society woman, was too much for her. Certainly Faraday, toward the end of the European jaunt, was thoroughly fed up with her, and wrote from Rome on February 23, 1815, to a close friend: ". . . but Lady Davy . . . likes to show her authority and at first I found her extremely earnest in mortifying me. This occasioned quarrels between us, at each of which I gained ground, and she lost it; for the frequency [of the quarrels] made me care nothing about them, and weakened her authority, and after each she behaved in a milder manner." Perhaps Lady Davy had overstepped the limit of being a "difficult" woman with Faraday; my friends tell me that one then becomes an "impossible" person!

SCIENTIFIC GENIUS AND MARRIAGE

Faraday himself, to judge by his letters and diaries, was very fortunate in his own ultimate choice of a wife. But clearly this does not always hold true for the great men of science. In his book on Rumford, Sanborn Brown tells us that: "On finishing his experiment, [Rumford] happened to glance out of the window in time to see Madame [his wife], with the aid of her maids, just completing the task of pouring boiling water over all his prize beds of roses. It was obvious that two people who would go to such lengths to annoy each other were hardly capable of living together very long." It seems too that James Clerk Maxwell's wife was not the most lovable of people. In correspondence between Maxwell's contemporaries, Mrs. Maxwell was often referred to as "that woman," and an apparently quite typical remark of hers was that reported when she said to her husband one evening in Cambridge: "James, it's time you went home, you are beginning to enjoy yourself." Sir George Thomson, distinguished physicist, son of the third Cavendish Professor at Cambridge, the renowned J. J. Thomson ("J. J."), has also been kind enough to tell me in a letter some impressions of Mrs. Maxwell which his own mother acquired. He says: "Everybody has agreed that Maxwell was a man of quite exceptionally lovable and, if you like, saintly character, but that Mrs. Maxwell, although no doubt she had her points was, to put it bluntly, a difficult woman. No doubt she had her trials as has everybody, but so undoubtedly had her husband. I think she somewhat softened in the years after his [Maxwell's] death when my mother knew her well, but she was not, even at her best, an easy woman." Whittaker[2] tells us that one of Maxwell's students referred to Mrs. Maxwell as "his terrible wife," that she "wanted Maxwell to live as a country gentleman—hunting, shooting and fishing," and that "she was rude to his scientific friends."

On the other hand, perhaps the natural tendency of biographers to idealize their subjects in all respects may have led Campbell and Garnett to write in their *Life of Maxwell:* "In February 1858 he announced his betrothal to Katherine Mary Dewar, and they were married early in the following June. . . . The correspondence of these months and the poems then written contain the record of feelings which in the years that followed were transfused in action and embodied in a married life which can only be spoken of as one of unexampled devotion."

Ah well, maybe it was the hand of Providence that sent these creative men their "difficult" wives; perhaps they were partly *driven* to their creative work to get away from the nagging! Of course the women in turn may argue that the boot is on the other foot, and that it is just these geniuses themselves who are so awkward to live with, that a wife can be hardly anything but "difficult." Perhaps this might well have been so with Rumford, but rather unlikely for Maxwell; from all the impressions we have of Maxwell, he was a rather gentle and lovable man.

Apart from the frustrations of frequent encounters with Lady Davy (whose personality has diverted us into this digression on genius and marriage), the tour of Europe must have been a remarkable experience for Faraday. It is clear from his private letters how much he missed his family and friends, and indeed this one trip abroad seems to have been the only time that Faraday left England, or even ventured far from London at all. On the extended journey through France, Italy, and back to England via Germany and Belgium, Davy met many European scientists and carried out a number of experiments with Faraday's help. In Paris, Davy was received by Ampère, Gay-Lussac, Humboldt, and others. When they were there, Davy made an analysis of some material given to him by Ampère, and identified a new chemical element present, which he called iodine. In Genoa Davy made some experiments on the "torpedo-fish," which can give rather powerful electric shocks. As a matter of fact, it is still of interest to this day how this remarkable fish manages to store and deliver these quite large electric charges at a considerable voltage.

The party also spent some time in Florence, and a major purpose of their visit there was to use a large lens belonging to the Grand Duke of Tuscany. With this lens Davy focused the rays of the sun onto a diamond which was placed on a platinum cup in a globe filled with oxygen, and Faraday in his diaries records the successful experiment: "Today we made the grand experiment of burning the diamond, and certainly the phenomena presented were extremely beautiful and interesting. . . . On a sudden, Sir H. Davy observed the diamond to burn visibly, and when removed from the focus it was found to be in a state of active and rapid combustion. The diamond glowed brilliantly with a scarlet light inclining to purple, and when placed in the dark continued to burn for about four minutes." Davy proved from this experiment that a diamond was just made of carbon. The experiment is really surprisingly topical, for today solar "furnaces" using mirrors or other devices to collect and focus radiation from the sun are often used to reach very high temperatures; moreover it was only a few years ago that artificial diamonds were successfully synthesized from carbon under intense pressures at high temperatures.

That a diamond and the so-called lead (which is graphite) in a pencil can look so different and yet both be made up of nothing but carbon atoms is in itself a most remarkable fact of nature, and also offers an example of the vital importance of *structure* in solid bodies. In a diamond the carbon atoms are arranged in an unending lattice structure, where each carbon atom is surrounded by four other carbon atoms. This unending regular array of carbon atoms is then responsible for the particular properties of diamond; in general, the stone is extremely strong, but as the whole lattice has a cubic symmetry, there are certain planes which are weaker than others and it is on these planes that, if a crack is once started, a diamond can be split. On the other hand, in graphite the carbon atoms are arranged in more or less flat layers and these layers can move fairly readily over one another. This ability of these layers to move freely gives graphite its particular properties as a lubricant.

Another particularly interesting example of the importance of structure is the element tin. Normally speaking we think of tin as a white, shiny metal and so indeed it usually is. But if we cool it down sufficiently and trigger off the reaction suitably, a piece of metallic tin will steadily transform into a grayish powder known naturally enough as gray tin, whose properties, such as the electrical conductivity, are very different from those of metallic tin. The reaction is quite reversible, for if you heat up the gray tin again above about 20°C. it will turn back to the metallic state. All that has happened to cause this remarkable change is that the tin atoms find it energetically more profitable, when the temperature is low enough, to take up a different structural arrangement in relation to one another as compared with the arrangement preferred at higher temperatures. Today the field of structural analysis, which involves particularly the use of X-rays for determining

[1] *Michael Faraday.*

The Royal Institution of Great Britain, London, sometime about 1840.

[3] *Humphry Davy. From a portrait in the Royal Society of London.*

[4] *Some of Humphry Davy's apparatus at the Royal Institution, London. a. (top) Specimens of safety lamps. b. (bottom) Apparatus for use in electrolysis.*

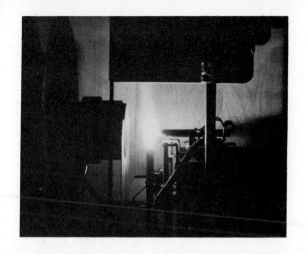

[5] *A small arc lamp for use in laboratory work. a. (top) The arc has been "struck" between the carbon rods, and the discharge emits an intense white light. b. (bottom) The arc has been extinguished so that no current is now passing between the carbon electrodes.*

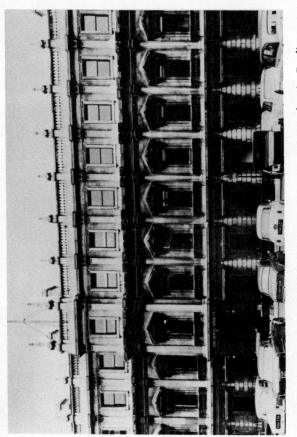

[6] *The present-day premises of the Royal Society of London in Burlington House, Piccadilly, London.*

The Obligation of the Fellows of the Royal Society.

We who have hereunto subscribed, do hereby promise each for himself that we will endeavour to promote the Good of the Royal Society for advancing Natural Knowledge, and to pursue the ends for which the same was founded. That we will be present at the meetings of the said Society as often as conveniently we can, especially at the Anniversary Elections and upon extraordinary occasions, and that we will observe the Statutes and Orders of the said Society. Provided that whensoever any of us shall signify to the President, under his hand, that he desires to withdraw from the Society, he shall be free from this Obligation for the future.

[7] *The signature of Humphry Davy in the Charter Book of the Royal Society. a. (top) Davy's signature. b. (bottom) The page of the Charter Book which includes Davy's signature.*

[8] *The signature of Michael Faraday in the Charter Book of the Royal Society. a. (top) Faraday's signature. b. (bottom) The page of the Charter Book which includes Faraday's signature.*

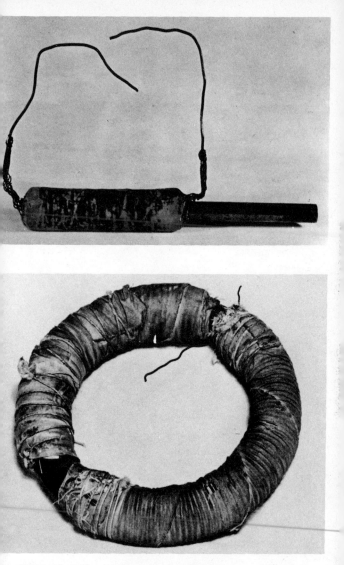

[9] *a. (top) One of the coils used by Faraday in his experiments on electromagnetism. b. (bottom) One of the coils used by Faraday in his experiments, and sketched in the page of his notes reproduced in Plate 10.*

Aug 29th 1831

Expts on the production of Electricity from Magnetism &c

Have had an iron ring made (soft iron) iron round each way
thick of ring 6 inches in external diameter. Wound many
coils of copper wire round one half the coils being separated
by twine & calico — there were 3 lengths of wire each about 24
feet long and they could be connected as one length or used
as separate lengths. By trial with a trough each was
insulated from the other. Will call this side of the ring
A   on the other side but separated by an
interval was wound wire in two pieces
together amounting to about 60 feet in
length the direction being as with the former
coils this side call B.

Charged a battery of 10 pr plates 4 inches square. Made
the coil on B side one coil and connected its extremities by
a copper wire passing to a distance and just over a magnetic
needle (3 feet from iron ring) then immersed the end of one of the
pieces on A side with battery. immediately a sensible effect on needle
It oscillated & settled at last in original position. On breaking
connection of A side with Battery again a disturbance
of the needle

Made all the wires on A side one coil and sent one
current from battery through the whole. Effect on needle much
stronger than before.

The effect on the needle then but a very small part of
that which the wire communicating directly with the battery
could produce

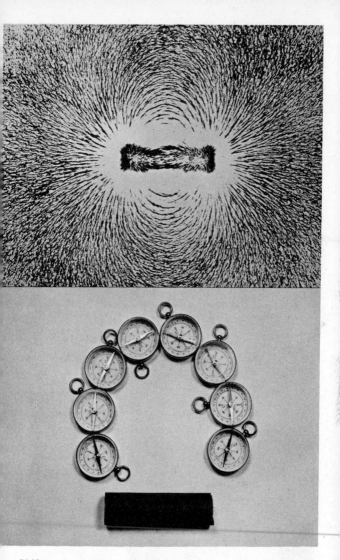

[11] a. (top) Pattern produced by iron filings when sprinkled on a sheet of paper placed over a strong bar magnet. b. (bottom) Illustrating how a compass needle will point along the "lines of force" produced by a magnet.

[12] *Engraving of Michael Faraday from the National Portrait Gallery reference portfolios.*

MICHAEL FARADAY

BORN 22 SEPTEMBER

1791

DIED 25 AUGUST

1867

SARAH - HIS WIFE

BORN 7 JANUARY

1800

DIED 6 JANUARY

1879

[13] *Gravestone of Michael Faraday in Highgate Cemetery, London*

atomic arrangements, is a tremendously important field for both physics and chemistry.

THE ROYAL SOCIETY OF LONDON

In Faraday's life as a scientist three events stand out like milestones in time, at roughly ten-year intervals. There was first the lengthy visit to Europe with Davy, which began in 1813 when Faraday was twenty-two. Ten years later, in 1823, election to Fellowship of the Royal Society of London formally recognized his position in science. Lastly in 1831, when Faraday was forty, came his prime achievement, the discovery of electromagnetic induction for which, above all, he is famous.

Election to the Royal Society of London (Plates 6, 7, and 8), which to this day is most important to British scientists, has been a treasured honor for a remarkably long time. Faraday himself ran into considerable obstacles in connection with candidacy but felt, as we shall see, that it was worth taking much trouble to ensure his election. Faraday recalls (perhaps somewhat wryly) the importance of gaining his Fellowship when, in later life, remembering the many honors he had received, he said: "One title, namely, that of F.R.S. [Fellow of the Royal Society], was sought and paid for; all the rest were spontaneous offerings of kindness and goodwill from the bodies named"; and in a letter close to the time of his election, he wrote: ". . . I am delighted by the hope I have of being honoured by Fellowship with the Society [The Royal Society]; and I thank you sincerely for your promise of support in my election, because I know you would not give it unless you sincerely thought me a fit person to be admitted. I am, Sir, your obliged and obedient servant, M. Faraday." (To Henry Warburton, August 29, 1823) In particular, election to the Royal Society meant, for

Faraday, full recognition of his ability and capacity as an independent scientist. In his own words, "I was by no means in the same relation as to scientific communication with Sir Humphry Davy after I became a Fellow of the Royal Society as before that period; . . ."

The official founding of the Royal Society of London is taken as the year 1660, and it recently commemorated its Tercentenary in London (in 1960) when scientists gathered from all over the world to show their respect, and to take part in the celebrations. The Society is one of the oldest scientific societies in the world, and has continued its existence unbroken through these three hundred years. Its first patron at its founding was King Charles II, and the Society chose as its motto, *"Nullius in Verba,"* which roughly translated means, "Don't take anybody's word for it." This motto was intended to express firmly and clearly that The Royal Society of London for Improving Natural Knowledge (as its full title goes) would foster and deal with critical and skeptical scientific development, based firmly on experimental evidence at all points, and not depending on arbitrary authority or dogma in any way. This outlook surely seems rather natural in science today, but it was a much more daring and revolutionary concept some three hundred years ago, when it was far more usual for men to appeal to the authority of ancient philosophers, or of the orthodox Church, than to feel bound to find things out for themselves. We may tend to pride ourselves that we are much more advanced in our outlook today, but before we get too uppish we should perhaps ask ourselves whether we now let the "authority" of Hollywood or of the Great Advertisers take the place of the authorities of old. I really do not think it is any more ludicrous to believe that stones will fall through the air in some particular way or other just because Aristotle said so, than it is to believe that some kind of hair oil will make you vastly popular just because some football or baseball player says so!

Among early Fellows of the Royal Society of London were such famous men as Isaac Newton, Christopher Wren, and Robert Hooke. The number of Fellows elected each year to the Society is strictly limited, and today a maximum of twenty-five in all may be elected annually; these are chosen from scientists, resident anywhere in the world, who are British subjects, or citizens of Eire (except as noted below). The elections have to cover all fields of physical science, mathematics, engineering, and the biological sciences, and the complaint is sometimes heard that only 1.88 mathematicians, say, are elected each year. The total Fellowship of the Society today numbers around six hundred, and one should not pretend that everyone elected now, or in the past, is a man of lasting distinction. What the Society probably can say with some pride is that, practically speaking, no really first-class man who is eligible as a scientist has failed to be elected. And, moreover, the Royal Society has often been able to spot the really brilliant men quite early, and elect them while they are still young. Thus, although a man *typically* is between forty-five and fifty years old when elected to the Royal Society of London, P. A. M. Dirac, who is world famous as a theoretical physicist, was elected when he was only twenty-seven. The Royal Society also elects three or four Foreign Members each year, and this membership is regarded as a very high honor indeed. In 1962 this body of distinguished Foreign Members included Hans Bethe, Niels Bohr, Peter Debye, Otto Hahn, Werner Heisenberg, Lise Meitner, Linus Pauling, Karl Siegbahn, and Harold Urey.

Following the example of the Royal Society of London, other Royal Societies have been founded in the past in various parts of the British Commonwealth;

the Royal Society of Canada was founded in 1883,
while the Royal Society of Edinburgh, in Scotland, has
quite a distinguished history of its own since its founding almost two hundred years ago in 1783. Faraday,
Maxwell, and Kelvin were all elected to the Royal Society of London in their turn, and Maxwell and Kelvin
were also Fellows of the Royal Society of Edinburgh—
indeed, Lord Kelvin thrice held the presidency of that
Society. Lord Kelvin later was elected to the presidency
of the Royal Society of London, perhaps the highest
scientific honor that Great Britain has to offer.

FARADAY'S ELECTION TO THE ROYAL SOCIETY

Faraday's own election to the Royal Society of London was not without its difficulties. First, he had to fight
a charge of plagiarism, which is regarded as a more
heinous offense in science perhaps than in almost any
other profession. Secondly, and sad to relate, it turned
out that Humphry Davy himself at first opposed very
strongly Faraday's election; and since at that time Davy
was President of the Royal Society, the situation for
Faraday must have been rather tricky, to put it mildly.
The story is a bit involved, and I must first digress a
little.

Although Faraday's greatest discovery in electromagnetism did not come until 1831, he had been interested in electricity and magnetism for a number of
years before that, and it was this early work that
led almost directly to the charge of plagiarism. After
the invention of the voltaic cell, from about 1800,
work could go ahead on experiments using steady currents of electricity. In 1819 the Danish physicist Hans
Christian Oersted (1777–1851) discovered that a wire
carrying an electric current could deflect a magnet
(such as a compass needle), and shortly afterward the

great French physicist and mathematician André Marie Ampère (1775–1836) investigated in detail the physical laws involved. The physical picture became clear that when an electric current flows in a conductor it produces a magnetic field around the conductor, and in this way it will interact with any *other* magnet in the neighborhood. Hence the effects that Oersted found. Moreover, if we have two wires carrying electric currents, then each wire will act as a magnet, and since magnets exert forces on each other, so will the two wires carrying currents exert forces on one another; the detailed law expressing this interaction is sometimes known as the Biot-Savart Law.†

It was essentially this chain of events that ultimately led Faraday to his prime discovery in electromagnetism. Very roughly speaking we might say that the train of thought which drove Faraday on for several years could be summarized in this way:

(1) A magnet will influence (act on) another magnet.

(2) An electric current can produce a magnetic field.

(3) An electric current can thus influence (act on) another electric current.

(4) So, to complete the story, can we produce an electric current from a magnet somehow, as the inverse action to (2)?

The solution of this last question is embodied in Faraday's discovery of electromagnetic induction, but this was not to come for some years yet (1831). But in April 1821, (and here we get back to the plagiarism story) a Dr. Wollaston[3] had visited Davy's laboratory at the Royal Institution in London, and Faraday heard some discussion of possible electromagnetic effects on

† Jean Baptiste Biot (1774–1862) and Felix Savart (1791–1841), both French physicists.

wires carrying electric currents. Some months later Faraday made experiments of his own in connection with an article he was writing, and discovered that he could make a wire carrying a current rotate around a magnet. He thought it wise before publishing his experiments to see Dr. Wollaston, but apparently Wollaston was out of town, and in Faraday's own words: ". . . by an error of judgment the paper was published without any allusion to [Wollaston's] notions and intentions." It then appears that very soon remarks were made ". . . affecting [Faraday's] honour and honesty." In October and November of 1821 Faraday tried to clear up these charges, and subsequently visited Wollaston himself. The subject seems to have come to the fore again in 1823 when Humphry Davy read a paper to the Royal Society on electromagnetism, and once more Faraday felt very unhappy, saying: "Thus, I was unjustly subjected to some degree of annoyance, and the more so because this happened . . . during the time that my name was before the Royal Society as a candidate for the Fellowship. I do not believe that anyone willingly was the cause of this state of things, but all seemed confusion, and generally to my disadvantage." Faraday was officially proposed on May 1, 1823, for Fellowship of the Royal Society, and he now had to make considerable efforts to exonerate himself of suspicion of scientific dishonesty in relation to Wollaston's work; Wollaston, moreover, was at that time a Vice-President of the Royal Society. Faraday managed to clear his name adequately, and it is satisfying that Wollaston's signature was one of the first to appear on Faraday's proposal for Fellowship, which read: "Mr. Michael Faraday, a gentleman eminently conversant in chemical science, and author of several papers, which have been published in the *Transactions* of the Royal Society, being desirous of becoming a Fellow thereof, we, whose names are undersigned, do of our personal knowledge recommend him as highly deserving that honour, and likely to become a useful and valuable member."

However, Faraday's difficulties were not over by any means. As Humphry Davy himself now decided to oppose Faraday's election, and since Davy was in fact President of the Royal Society at the time, it might have been hard to imagine a worse omen! In the *Philosophical Transactions* of the Royal Society of London for the year 1823 there appear two or three papers by Faraday himself, and also one by Humphry Davy, on experiments concerned with the production of liquids, such as liquid chlorine, from chemical reactions producing appropriate vapors. Faraday seems to have annoyed Davy by publishing the results of some experiments in this field without, Davy felt, giving him sufficient credit. Davy died in 1829, and some years later, in 1836, when Faraday was reading an account of Davy's life, he felt he must explain the situation, and closed a letter on the subject by saying: "I have never remarked upon or denied Sir H. Davy's right to his share of the condensation of chlorine or the other gases; on the contrary, I think that I long ago did him full 'justice' in the papers themselves. How could it be otherwise? He saw and revised the manuscripts; through his hands they went to the Royal Society, of which he was President at the time; and he saw and revised the printer's proofs. . . . All this activity in the condensing of gases was simultaneous with the electro-magnetic affair; and I had learned to be cautious upon points of right and priority. . . ." The general situation seems fairly clear. On the one hand we have a very keen, dedicated, and probably quite ambitious young man of exceptional talent who was climbing the steps to fame from complete obscurity at a remarkable rate. Although it seems quite certain that no one today would dream of accusing Faraday of a shred of dishonesty, he was probably not as tactful as he might have been in showing courtesy to Davy and Wollaston as older and more senior men when he was anxious to get ahead and have his work published. But on the other hand this is a most natural, and surely forgivable fault in a young man of real promise.

PRIORITY AND CREDIT FOR DISCOVERY

Now it is often assumed that scientists generally are unemotional and dry people, and entirely logical, reasonable men. Not so. They must certainly try very often to be logical and unemotional if possible, when engaged directly in their profession, and when actively making experiments or working out their significance. But the very urge that will make men devote long hours to work that is demanding and exhausting, and that may well come to nothing in the end, is bound to be an emotional drive of some kind or another. The basic drive to try to create something original probably does not vary too much from man to man, be he scientist, artist, or writer. We do not expect a poet or composer to take lightly his works being published under someone else's name. So is it any less surprising that a scientist feels just as keenly his right to be credited with whatever he discovers himself? There have been long and bitter quarrels down the years between scientists about priority for discoveries or scientific progress of one kind and another. Perhaps the most famous is that between Newton and Leibniz on priority for the invention of differential calculus. To some folk, such concern with priority and the credit for discovery seems rather childish or at least inconsistent with the "glory of science." But to me, at least, it seems a very natural and normal consequence of the fact that it is *men* who are doing the science; were it not for the emotional urge to lay bare something which no one else has done before, there might well be *no* psychological drive to make men do science at all. In brief, despite Milton's somewhat critical comments about fame‡, if men did not care deeply about being credited for their discoveries, they might well have no desire to make any at all.

Not only may Davy have resented what he felt was some loss of credit for his ideas, but he was probably only human in feeling somewhat jealous of this brilliant young man's rapid development. Nevertheless, considering that Davy himself was only forty-five at this time, was President of the Royal Society, and had been made a baronet[4] in 1818, it was certainly not very generous of him to resent Faraday's scientific growth, but I repeat that I think it was very human; it was probably also evidence of tacit recognition by Davy that Faraday was a man of unique distinction (and therefore some indirect "threat" to Davy's own high standing). Be that as it may, Faraday tells us that: "Sir H. Davy told me I must take down my certificate [of proposal for Fellowship]. I replied that I had not put it up; . . . Then he said, I as President will take it down. I replied that I was sure Sir H. Davy would do what he thought was for the good of the Royal Society." One does not come across too many signs of lively humor in Faraday's remarks, but I think he made that last reply with his tongue in his cheek! Within a month or two, Davy's objections faded, and Faraday was duly elected in January 1824 to the Royal Society.

Davy himself was a man of strong emotions which

‡ Fame is the spur that clear spirit doth raise
  (That last infirmity of noble mind)
  To scorn delights, and live laborious days; . . .
            Lycidas by John Milton

were often difficult for him to cope with; he had a deep interest in literature and poetry, and was quite intimate with the poets William Wordsworth (1770–1850) and Samuel Taylor Coleridge (1772–1834). The poet and historian, Robert Southey (1774–1843), said of Davy: "He had all the elements of poetry, he only wanted the art," and it was Davy who led Wordsworth to write: "Poetry is the first and last of all knowledge—it is as immortal as the heart of man. . . . The remotest discoveries of the chemist, the botanist, and mineralogist, will be as proper objects of the poet's art as any upon which it can be employed." Coleridge's description of how Davy compared with contemporaries in London, was most vivid: "Why, Davy can eat them all, . . . there is an energy, an elasticity, in his mind which enable him to seize on and analyze all questions, pushing them to their legitimate consequences. Every subject in Davy's mind has the principle of vitality. Living thoughts spring up like turf under his feet."§

When we recall, moreover, the disdainful manner in which Lady Davy treated Faraday during the trip to Europe, one may guess that Davy also had his problems in dealing with Lady Davy herself. Finally, we should bear in mind that Davy's health broke down some years before he died in 1829, and sickness may also have played a part in giving him a somewhat jaundiced view of life at times. But in any case, it is to both Faraday's and Davy's credit that in later years Faraday always

§ These quotations are as given by Sir Harold Hartley, F.R.S., in his Wilkins Lecture to the Royal Society on Humphry Davy (Proc. Roy. Soc. A. 255, 153, 1960). This excellent study gives a very clear picture of Davy's remarkable productivity and insight. In Hartley's words: ". . . Faraday, consciously or unconsciously, owed much to these flashes of Davy's genius. Faraday with his skill in measurement, his patience and his unerring intuition gave precision and finality to Davy's tentative idea."

spoke in the highest praise of Sir Humphry Davy and was loath to hear any criticism of him.

FARADAY'S MARRIAGE

In Faraday's private life one would guess that the most important milestone was his marriage. In 1821, at twenty-nine years of age, he married Miss Sarah Barnard, whose family, like Faraday, belonged to the Sandemanian religious fellowship. Some of Faraday's letters, and those to his younger sister particularly, may seem a little heavy today, but to his wife-to-be he could write very charmingly, and his marriage, although childless like those of Clerk Maxwell and Lord Kelvin, appears to have been a most happy one. Many years later he wrote of himself: "On June 12, 1821, he married—an event which more than any other contributed to his earthly happiness and healthful state of mind. The union has continued for twenty-eight years, and has nowise changed, except in the depth and strength of its character." And when Faraday was seventy-one years old he wrote to his wife: "I long to see you, dearest, and to talk over things together, and call to mind all the kindness I have received. My head is full, and my heart also, but my recollection rapidly fails, even as regards the friends that are in the room with me. You will have to resume your old function of being a pillow to my mind, and a rest, a happy-making wife. . . . Dearest, I long to see and be with you, whether together or separate—Your husband, very affectionate —M. Faraday."

A year after his election to the Royal Society, Faraday was elected a Member of the Royal Institution and was also appointed Director of the Laboratory. It would seem that relations between Davy and Faraday must then have been quite cordial, for the Minutes of

the Royal Institution for February 7, 1825, record that
Sir H. Davy ". . . having stated that he considered the
talents and services of Mr. Faraday, assistant in the
laboratory, entitled to some mark of approbation from
the managers, and these sentiments having met the cordial concurrence of the board: Resolved that Mr. Faraday be appointed Director of the Laboratory under the
superintendence of the Professor of Chemistry."

THE DISCOVERY OF ELECTROMAGNETIC INDUCTION

We come now to the crowning achievement of Faraday's scientific career. Let us recapitulate the developments relating electricity and magnetism. In 1800,
Volta had made the first battery to provide a steady
flow of electricity—that is, an electric current—through
a conductor such as a metal wire. In 1819, Oersted
showed that an electric current flowing in a circuit
would cause a magnetic needle to deflect. Oersted's discovery demonstrated that electricity and magnetism
were intimately related, and Ampère went on to prove
that an electric current behaved exactly as a magnet
whose properties could be computed precisely from the
shape of the electric circuit and the amount of current
flowing in it. The problem that Faraday then tackled
was essentially the other side of the coin. If electricity
produced magnetism, surely magnetism should somehow produce electricity? In various experiments from
1824 he tried to find such a relationship but without
success, and finally came his triumph on August 29,
1831, when he was almost forty years old. Not long
ago I had occasion to ask several colleagues what they
felt was most characteristic of Faraday's work; I really
was trying to find out which experiments they felt were
his most important. All agreed that Faraday's crowning
achievement was his discovery of electromagnetic in-

duction, but one chemist friend also said in reply to my question: "Perseverance." Maxwell in an article that he wrote about Faraday in the Encyclopædia Britannica specifically mentions Faraday's persistence. Faraday's experiments, extending over many years, to discover how to generate electric effects from magnetism are surely a clear example of this perseverance and dogged determination—and indeed it was well rewarded.

The vital feature which Faraday finally discovered was that magnetism had to be *moving,* or *changing,* to generate an electric current in a neighboring circuit. This did not seem at all obvious in Faraday's day for, as Oersted and Ampère had shown, a *steady* electric current produced a *steady* magnetic effect around the circuit carrying the current. Also an electrostatically charged body (like the homely fountain pen which has been rubbed on one's sleeve) can induce a steady charge-distribution in other bodies (such as small pieces of paper) which are nearby. And also, of course, a permanent magnet whose magnetic properties may remain unchanged for many, many years will exert a steady force on another magnet, or a piece of iron. So it was very natural to assume that a steady electric current should somehow be generated if a wire were placed near or around a magnet, although perhaps a very strong magnet might be required. But all such attempts were doomed to failure. Today it is clear on very general grounds that this must be so, because if we could generate a steady electric current by simply wrapping a coil of wire somehow around a permanent magnet, then that current could be used to provide a continuous source of useful energy or work. On the other hand, a permanent magnet, made from suitable magnetized steel, will by its very name show no change in its magnetic properties over many years. Consequently, if such a magnet lay peacefully on a table, and a coil of wire placed around or near it in some fashion could in that way produce a steady current, we would ask immediately today where the energy or work to maintain the current was coming from. And indeed we would say with confidence that the Principle of Conservation of Energy (which we discuss again in Chapter IV on the life of Lord Kelvin) forbids any such thing to happen. But we must remember that this was almost a hundred and fifty years ago, and the general validity of such a law was very much less certain.[5] The vital secret really lies in appreciating that an electric current is not itself a *static* thing; we know with certainty today that a current is just a movement of electric charge. If we recast the question to read: If a moving (i.e., changing) electric charge can produce magnetic effects, how can we make a magnet produce electric effects?—then I think the probable answer becomes clear. We must see whether a moving magnet, or more generally some *changing* magnetic effect, can produce, or "induce," an electric current. This is indeed the basic answer to Faraday's problem, but let me repeat that it is clear to us today only because of the persevering work of pioneers such as Faraday and Maxwell. In Faraday's day it was far from obvious that electric currents in wires were moving charges, and it was not really until the end of last century that this conclusion became well established.

Actually, in Faraday's first successful experiment on electromagnetic induction he produced the necessary changing magnetic effect by switching on and off an electric current in a coil which was wound round part of a ring of iron, and he then observed an "induced" electric current in another quite *separate* coil of wire which was wound on the opposite side of the ring and quite insulated from the first coil.[6] But now let us turn to Faraday's words about these remarkable experiments, since his own laboratory records (Plate 10) read so clearly that the best we can do is to quote directly from them. In his notebook headed *Electrical Researches,* he wrote: "I have had an iron ring made (. . .) ⅞ths of an inch thick, and (. . .) six inches in external diameter. Wound many coils of copper round, . . . Will call this side of the ring A. On the other side, but separated by an interval, was wound wire (. . .) amounting to about sixty feet in length, the direction being as with the former coils. This side call B. [Plate 9a.] Charged a battery of ten pairs of plates four inches square . . . connected [the] extremities [of coil on B] by a copper wire passing to a distance, and just over a magnetic needle (three feet from wire ring), then connected the ends of . . . A side with battery: immediately a sensible effect on needle. It oscillated and settled at last in original position. On breaking connection of A side with battery, again a disturbance of the needle."

Faraday thus had shown that the passage of an electric current in one coil of wire could produce a momentary surge of electricity in another quite separate coil of wire if they were linked together by some magnetizable material (i.e., the iron ring). Faraday's report of this momentary and quite small disturbance of the magnetic needle was the first observation of what is known today as electromagnetic induction. One can also say that in that remarkable experiment Faraday had made, and tested successfully, the first electrical transformer.

If Faraday had continued switching the electric current on and off rhythmically in coil *A,* then he would have observed a rhythmic, or alternating, current induced in coil *B.* Today most of the electric power that is sent from one place to another travels *not* as a steady flow of current always in one direction (so-called direct current), but is generated and delivered as an oscillating or alternating current which, typically, changes its polarity, or direction of flow, fifty or sixty times every second. With such alternating current, which is produced readily from rotating generators (also based directly on Faraday's induction discoveries) we can readily change, or transform, an electric current at high voltage into a stronger current at low voltage, and *vice versa,* by using a transformer which is a very direct descendent of Faraday's first iron ring with two coils of wire. If we make coil *A* (which we would now call the primary of the transformer) of a few turns of heavy wire, and coil *B* (the secondary of the transformer) of many turns of quite fine wire, then a low voltage (but relatively high current) electric oscillation in the primary circuit will produce a rather high voltage (but relatively low current) oscillating electrical output in the secondary circuit. And we can do things just as well the other way round if we wish, so that we can have "step-up" and "step-down" transformers to supply us readily with electric power at any particular supply voltage we please. Broadly speaking, our efficient transmission of power over long distances by the familiar chains of pylons crossing the country depends for its success very directly on the use of transformers. At the generating end the voltage is stepped up (typically to about 100,000 volts) so that power can be sent long distances at this high voltage. (The current involved is correspondingly low, which is effectively what makes the process economical.) At the receiving end, in electric sub-stations and the like, the voltage is "stepped down," in transformers again, to values which are relatively safe to use in houses (typically about 100 or 200 volts), while of course the current at the same time has been automatically "stepped up" so that a very large number of consumers can be fed with the transmitted electric power.

Once Faraday had got on to the right track, his experiments proceeded very rapidly, and three weeks after the first success, writing to a friend named Phillips, he said: "I am busy just now again on electromagnetism, and I think I have got hold of a good thing, but can't say. It may be a weed instead of a fish that, after all my labour, I may at last pull up." On the fifth day of these experiments, October 17, 1831, Faraday for the first time produced an electric current directly from the action of a magnet alone. In his words: "A cylindrical bar magnet three-quarters of an inch in diameter, and eight inches and a half in length, had one end just inserted into the end of the helix cylinder (. . .); then it was quickly thrust in the whole length, and the *galvanometer* needle moved; then pulled out, and again the *needle moved,* but in the opposite direction [Plate 9b]. This effect was repeated every time the magnet was put in or out, and therefore a wave of electricity was so produced. . . ." And so it went. On October 28, he tells us that he ". . . made a copper disc turn round between the poles of the great horseshoe magnet of the Royal Society. The axis and edge of the disc were connected with a galvanometer. The galvanometer needle moved as the disc turned. . . ." These historic experiments are a foundation stone for the whole enormous field of electromagnetism today. Faraday in fact made the first transformer and dynamo, and his work was vital in leading James Clerk Maxwell some forty years later to his theory of electromagnetic radiation, from which today has developed the vast use of radio waves of one kind and another for communication and entertainment over the whole world.

THE IMPORTANCE OF FARADAY'S DISCOVERIES

Broadly speaking, we might summarize some of the important features of these discoveries by Faraday in electromagnetism as follows:

1. It now became possible to devise means for generating electric current continuously, and for as long as one pleased, by moving appropriate coils of wire through the influence (or the "field") of a magnet. This is precisely the fundamental principle of the rotary electrical generator or dynamo, and all our present vast networks of electric power stations, whether driven by coal, oil, or water power, in the end depend on this very principle.

2. Faraday had produced the satisfying answer to his question: "Electricity can produce magnetism; can magnetism produce electricity?"[7] On the whole, the universe of natural law has a great deal of symmetry about it, and we are always anxious to try to find reciprocal relations between effects such as: "If A can produce B, then B can produce A."

3. Faraday's discovery of electromagnetic induction, together with the general symmetry, or reciprocity, that results between electric and magnetic effects, was essential to Maxwell's subsequent prediction of self-sustaining electromagnetic waves which could propagate themselves through space.

It is well nigh unthinkable to try to visualize what our world of today would be like if there were no dynamos, electric motors, and no radio communication of any kind (nor for that matter, any television!). But the work of Michael Faraday was an utterly vital link in the chain of events that gave us all these developments, so truly one could say of Faraday: *"Si monumentum requiris, circumspice."*

Faraday worked feverishly while making these discoveries, and certainly every person who has been lucky enough to discover anything which is even a little new, knows that the time of discovery is at once the most fascinating and demanding. By November 29, 1831, Faraday was able to write from Brighton to his friend Phillips: "We are here to refresh. I have been working and writing a paper[;] that always knocks me up in health, but now I feel well again, and able to pursue my subject; and now I will tell you what it is about. The title will be, I think, 'Experimental Researches in Electricity':— I. On the Induction of Electric Currents; II. On the Evolution of Electricity from Magnetism; III. On a new Electrical Condition of Matter; IV. On Arago's** Magnetic Phenomena. There is a bill of fare for you; and, what is more, I hope it will not disappoint you. Now the pith of all this I must give you very briefly; the demonstrations you shall have in the paper when printed."

MAGNETIC AND ELECTRICAL LINES OF FORCE

Apart from the immediate and vital importance of Faraday's research in electromagnetic induction, the

** Dominique François Jean Arago (1786–1853) did early work on geodetic measurements. At the age of twenty-three he gained the Chair of Analytical Geometry at Ecole Polytecnique, and at age forty-four entered the Chamber of Deputies, and was also elected Perpetual Secretary of the Academy of Sciences and Director of the Observatory. According to the Encyclopædia Britannica, 1960, "Arago's fame as an experimenter and discoverer rests mainly on his contributions to magnetism and optics. He found . . . that a rotating plate of copper tends to communicate its motion to a magnetic needle suspended over it ('magnetism of rotation')."

discoveries also played an important part in leading him to the concept of "lines of force" as a physical picture of electric and magnetic forces and interactions. In turn Faraday's ideas influenced James Clerk Maxwell, who developed his comprehensive electromagnetic theory from which electromagnetic radiation through space was first predicted. If one places a magnet near iron filings on paper and then taps the paper, the filings quickly arrange themselves in a strikingly characteristic pattern of "lines" stretching from one pole of the magnet to the other (Plate 11a). Faraday was well aware of this behavior. He suggested that one should think (even in the absence of any actual iron filings) of these lines of force as extending permanently from the magnet and filling all the space around it. The force which a magnet could exert at any place in space (e.g., on another magnet or piece of iron) would then be determined by these lines of force. Thus, for example, if we put a small compass needle near a magnet, it would point along one of these "lines of force" (see Plate 11b), and, moreover, the intensity of the force would be determined by the density (i.e., the closeness together) of Faraday's lines of force.

The concept of these magnetic lines of force permanently pervading all the space around a magnetized body enabled Faraday mentally to avoid the notion of "action at a distance" (e.g., between two magnetized bodies), which was repugnant to him (and indeed to many other scientists in those days). We return to this question again in the next chapter dealing with Maxwell and his work; let us just say here that the idea of magnetic lines of force filling the space around a magnetic body, coupled with Faraday's later idea of similar electric lines of force produced by electrically charged bodies, was a most profitable one in at least two ways. First, it helped Faraday himself to think in a systematic fashion about his experiments, and so by understanding them in this way to go forward logically and productively to further experiments. Secondly, Maxwell, who read Faraday's "Experimental Researches" while still an undergraduate at Cambridge, and who had always a profound respect for Faraday's work, was stimulated by Faraday's ideas to work out ultimately the comprehensive theoretical model which provided physical science with Maxwell's beautiful electromagnetic theory.

In his letter to Phillips about his electromagnetic experiments, Faraday mentioned his need for rest and recuperation after an intense period of experimental work. The strains of prolonged concentration seem to have affected Faraday throughout his life; naturally enough, the effects became more severe and troublesome as he got older, although he lived to be more than seventy years old. Whittaker[8] also tells us that it was suspected that Faraday ". . . was suffering *inter alia* from mercury poisoning; in electric connections he made great use of cups of mercury, some of which would, no doubt, be spilt occasionally on the floor of the laboratory and ultimately vaporized. . . ." In September 1862, when Faraday was seventy-one, he wrote to Professor Schönbein†† (of Bâle in Switzerland), with whom he had corresponded for many years: "Again and again I tear up my letters, for I write nonsense. I cannot spell or write a line continuously. Whether I shall recover—this confusion—do not know. I will not write any more. My love to you."

In his later years Faraday declined the proposal of a knighthood and also the offer, made twice to him, of the presidency of the Royal Society; when he was sixty-six years old, he said to the man who became his

†† Christian Friedrich Schönbein, chemist (1790–1868), taught at the University of Bâle (or Basel) from 1828, and discovered ozone in 1840.

successor at the Royal Institution: "Tyndall,[9] I must remain plain Michael Faraday to the last; and let me now tell you that, if I accept the honour which The Royal Society desires to confer upon me, I would not answer for the integrity of my intellect for a single year." He was again clearly aware of increasing mental strain as he got older.

THE ART OF LECTURING

We recall that in 1825, the year after he was elected to the Royal Society of London, Faraday received the title of Director of the Laboratory at the Royal Institution, and in 1833 he became Fullerian Professor of Chemistry at the Royal Institution. Throughout his years at the Royal Institution Faraday, apart from his wide research activities, gave a great deal of conscientious attention to the art of lecturing and to arrangements for lectures on scientific topics; lectures given by distinguished scientists were, and are, an important function of the Royal Institution. In an early letter, written by Faraday when he was twenty-one, he says to his friend Abbott: ". . . I would by no means have a lecturer glued to the table or screwed on the floor. . . . [He] should appear easy and collected, undaunted and unconcerned, his thoughts about him, and his mind clear and free for the contemplation and description of his subject. . . . His whole behaviour should envince respect for his audience, and he should in no case forget that he is in their presence. . . . I do not approve of [a lecturer] reading [his matter]; at least not as he would a quotation or extract. He should deliver it in a ready and free manner, referring to his book merely as he would to copious notes, and not confining his tongue to the exact path there delineated, but digress as circumstances may demand or localities allow. . . . For the same reason (namely, that the audience should not grow tired), I disapprove of long lectures; one hour is long enough for anyone, nor should they be allowed to exceed that time." I have myself taught university and other classes for about twenty years now, and I certainly could not attempt to express more clearly what I believe are the essentials of good lecturing than Faraday has done here—and he said this at the age of twenty-one!

In a later letter to Abbott, Faraday discusses again the question of lecturing, and his comments show a keen perception of human failings, which, I imagine, could be rather disturbing to those around him. He writes: "A lecturer falls deeply beneath the dignity of his character when he descends so low as to angle for claps, and asks for commendation. . . . I have heard [a lecturer] dwell for a length of time on the extreme care and niceness that the experiment he will make requires. I have heard [a lecturer] hope for indulgence when no indulgence was wanted, and I have even heard him declare that the experiment now made cannot fail from its beauty, its correctness, and its application, to gain the approbation of all. . . ." Faraday's implied criticism could apply very well today, I think, to the habits of many M.C.'s on television and radio. Faraday saw clearly how important it was for a lecturer to have some spontaneity and to use illustrations from items or objects that might be readily at hand, and he goes on: " 'Tis well, too, when the lecturer has the ready wit and the presence of mind to turn any casual circumstance to an illustration of his subject. Any particular circumstance that has become table-talk for the town, any local advantages or disadvantages, any trivial circumstance that may arise in company, give great force to illustrations aptly drawn from them, and please the audience highly, as they conceive they perfectly understand them." Since Faraday had done little lecturing himself at this time, his comments show clearly that he must have been a sensitive and very attentive listener. However, his inherent modesty also showed up when, some two or three years later, he wrote once more: ". . . with respect to my remarks on lectures, I perceive I am but a mere tyro in the art, . . ." But in fact Faraday proved himself to be a most skilled and capable lecturer. When, on Davy's suggestion, Faraday, at the age of thirty-four, was appointed Director of the Laboratory, weekly meetings of the Members of the Royal Institution were started as an experiment. Faraday became principally responsible for these meetings, and the Friday evening "Discourses" have continued to this day as a regular feature.‡‡ A year later, in 1826, Christmas Lectures for Children, or "Lectures adapted to a juvenile auditory" as they were called, were inaugurated, and since then have remained a very popular and valuable part of the Royal Institution program.

Quite recently, Sir Lawrence Bragg, the present Director of the Royal Institution, has begun to broaden the scope of the program, and Faraday's example of lectures on scientific subjects aimed directly at young people has also been followed in many places. So, for example, in Oxford University about half a dozen lectures, particularly for young people, were arranged each year around Christmastime, covering such fields as Exploration, Natural History, and Low Temperature Physics, and at the National Research Council in Ottawa we also followed Faraday's lead by starting some years ago a program of Christmas lectures for children. Perhaps I might mention that at such children's lec-

‡‡ Professor Sanborn Brown, whose biography of Rumford I have mentioned, was invited to deliver a "Discourse" in May 1963.

tures one usually found many adults listening and our lectures in Ottawa were advertised ... intended for "Children from 8 to 80"! In case the word child should insult anyone, let me say that the vital aspect, as Faraday himself well appreciated, is that children usually have not yet become blasé or bored, and are still willing to be surprised and to wonder at things about them. I sometimes think that the most dangerous thing parents may do to children today is to kill this sense of wonder, and that we have some young people growing up now who are old and bored before they are seventeen.

THE FINAL YEARS

Faraday must have given a great number of lectures throughout his life; his last lecture to the Royal Institution was on Friday, June 20, 1862, when he was seventy years old. His personal notes to explain why at last he was about to retire are very touching. Here they are: "Personal explanation,—years of happiness here, but time of retirement; *loss of memory* and *physical endurance of the brain.* 1. Causes—*hesitation and uncertainty* of the convictions which the speaker has to urge. 2. *Inability to draw* upon the mind for the treasures of knowledge it has previously received. 3. *Dimness,* and forgetfulness of one's former *self-standard* in respect of right, *dignity,* and *self-respect.* 4. Strong duty of *doing justice to others,* yet inability to do so. *Retire.*" He was unable to continue in the middle of his lecture and said that he feared that he had "been with them too long." He went to his chair and the audience rose in a moving scene to give him a prolonged ovation. In 1858 Faraday had been asked to accept one of Queen Victoria's Grace and Favour Houses at Hampton Court,[10] and it was there that he died nine years later on August 25,

1867, at the age of seventy-five; his grave is in Highgate Cemetery (Plate 13). His niece wrote on the day following his death: "My dear Dr. Bence Jones,—Our cares are over; our beloved one is gone. He passed away from this life quietly and peacefully yesterday afternoon. Almost immediately after you saw him, a little more than a fortnight ago, he became weaker, and has said very little to us or taken much notice of anything from that time; but still we did not expect the change until an hour or two before it happened. He died in his chair, in his study; and we feel we could desire nothing better for him than what has occurred. . . ."

I think it is quite common for scientists today to think of Faraday as first and foremost an experimentalist, and of Clerk Maxwell as a theoretician. It is true that their prime achievements fall after this fashion: namely, Faraday's experimental discovery of electromagnetic induction and what went with it, and Clerk Maxwell's superb electromagnetic theory. But for both men that is only part of the story, and Faraday's successor as Superintendent at the Royal Institution, John Tyndall, wrote:

"Faraday's principal researches, . . . are all connected by an undercurrent of speculation. Theoretic ideas were the very sap of his intellect—the source from which all his strength as an experimenter was derived. While once sauntering with him through the Crystal Palace at Sydenham I asked him what directed his attention to the magnetization of light. . . . He had certain views regarding the unity and convertibility of natural forces; certain ideas regarding the vibrations of light and their relations to the lines of magnetic force; these views and ideas drove him to investigation. And so it must always be; the great experimentalist must ever be the habitual theorist, whether or not he gives to his theories formal enunciation. . . . Faraday was more than a philosopher; he was a prophet and often wrought by an inspiration to be understood by sympathy alone." Despite the tremendous and exciting developments in physical science over the past fifty years, it seems to me a rather sad consequence that a quite marked separation between so-called experimental physics and theoretical physics has developed in some quarters. I think one can say confidently that neither Faraday, nor Maxwell, nor Kelvin, would have had much sympathy with such an outlook, and would all have agreed that a physicist must always make experiments *and* think.

The most natural memorial to a physicist is the naming of some unit of measurement after him. Faraday has the rather rare distinction that two units embody his name: the faraday, which refers to the amount of electrical charge carried by the standard quantity (1 gram-molecule) of an ionized substance, and the farad, which is the basis for the measurement of electrical capacity in practical units.

In his earlier years Michael Faraday summarized his own ideas of what a philosopher should be; his words seem to be suitable to describe his own life. "The philosopher should be a man willing to listen to every suggestion, but determined to judge for himself. He should not be biased by appearances; have no favourite hypothesis; be of no school; and in doctrine have no master. He should not be a respecter of persons, but of things. Truth should be his primary object. If to these qualities be added industry, he may indeed hope to talk within the veil of the temple of nature."

NOTES

1. Great Britain is one of the few countries today where you can still be honored in this sort of way by the state. When William Thomson, whom we talk about in Chapter IV (but quite unrelated to Benjamin Thompson), was made a baron by Queen Victoria in 1896, he chose to call himself Lord Kelvin, and took the name Lord Kelvin after the River Kelvin, which meanders through Glasgow, passing close to the University of Glasgow where he taught for very many years. Much more recently Professor F. A. Lindemann of Oxford University was made a baron by Winston Churchill's government during the last war, and he chose to call himself Lord Cherwell, because a small river, the Cherwell, flows through Oxford.

2. E. T. Whittaker: *History of the Theories of Aether and Electricity* (Edinburgh: Thomas Nelson and Sons, Ltd., 1951). We shall refer to this exhaustive and delightful treatise subsequently as "Whittaker—1951."

3. William Hyde Wollaston, 1766–1828. Apart from working in what was then the very new field of electromagnetism, Wollaston appears to have been a most productive scientist. According to the Columbia Encyclopedia it was he who discovered in 1802 the dark lines in the (solar) spectrum usually named after Joseph von Fraunhofer (1787–1826), who studied and mapped these lines, and in 1803 Wollaston also discovered the elements palladium and rhodium. Wollaston was a Vice-President of the Royal Society.

4. When Davy was knighted in 1812, he became Sir Humphry Davy (and his wife received the courtesy title of Lady Davy); however, a knighthood "dies" with its holder. The next honor up the ladder, so to speak, is a baronetcy; the form of address remained

Sir Humphry Davy, but the title could now be inherited by his heirs, if any. In order to be addressed as "Lord So-and-So" it is necessary to acquire a barony.

5. Today the Laws of Conservation of Energy and Momentum are regarded as essential foundation stones of physical science. If some process turned up which appeared at first sight to violate either of these laws, then we would probably suggest instead that some additional momentum or energy was actually involved to balance up the situation, but that for some reason we were, for the present at any rate, unable to observe directly this energy or momentum contribution. Essentially this is just what happened when the neutrino was first introduced by Wolfgang Pauli into physics. The neutrino has now been observed (indeed, it now seems, two different types!), but when it was first "born," so to speak, it was not observable and its existence was simply *postulated* to avoid an apparent violation of these basic laws in certain interactions or "collisions" involving fundamental particles in physics.

6. According to Whittaker (1951, Vol. 1, p. 171): ". . . this great discovery was only narrowly missed by Ampère; cf. S. P. Thompson, Phil. Mag., *39*, (1895), p. 534."

7. The name of Joseph Henry (1797–1878) should also be mentioned here. Quoting from the Columbia Encyclopedia: "He [Henry] discovered self-inductance, and the unit of inductance is for that reason often called the henry. Independently of Michael Faraday he discovered the principle of the induced current, basic to the dynamo, transformer, and many other devices; Henry's experiments in this field may have [even] antedated Faraday's detection of the current, but he acknowledged the priority of Faraday, who had published his results earlier." Joseph Henry was a most productive physicist, and from 1846 he was the first Secretary and Director of the Smithsonian Institution.

8. Whittaker, op. cit., p. 128.

9. John Tyndall (1820–93), physicist. In 1853 he became Professor of Natural Philosophy (physics) at the Royal Institution and, on Faraday's death, Superintendent. His research work lay in sound and radiation, and he was also particularly interested in Alpine glaciers. Like Faraday, he was very capable at lecturing for the layman.

10. Houses, or apartments, granted rent-free by the Crown to specially selected families. Originally these were chiefly widows or children of those who, for example, had served in the armed forces. Later, distinction in other professions became a qualification.

Chapter III

JAMES CLERK MAXWELL

CHILDHOOD IN SCOTLAND

James Clerk Maxwell (Plate 14) was born on June 13, 1831, at No. 14 India Street, Edinburgh. Plate 15 shows the street as it is today, together with a close view of the Memorial Stone on the wall of 14 India Street. Scottish towns and cities change more slowly than do their North American counterparts; apart from the automobiles, I suppose India Street looks much the same today as it did when Maxwell was born. When people built houses in Scotland, they built them to last. (They had to, because even the most loyal Scot has to admit that the Scottish climate is not the most benign in the world!) Broad streets like India Street flanked by solid houses built of gray stone are very common in the older parts of Edinburgh, and indeed in many Scottish towns. As a matter of fact, older Edinburgh would well be described as "Gray Edinburgh." North America at its worst calls to my mind a brassy, merciless sun blazing down fiercely in midsummer, where buildings, streets, and cars seem either frighteningly new or very suddenly shabbily old. At the other extreme I tend to recall Edinburgh in midwinter where a weak, tepid, reddish sun just struggles over the horizon, and casts a rather feeble light (even at midday) after being filtered through the smoke and low-lying clouds. Little wonder that Edinburgh is known to its friends as "Auld Reekie" (Scots for "Old Smokey").

Scotsmen are a funny breed, obstinate, determined, often rather reserved ("dour"), but, when driven to make a comment, usually rather direct in what they have to say. One wonders how much geography and climate determine the character of a people, and perhaps one should remember that Edinburgh is just north of Moscow's latitude, and if transported to Canada would find itself well up on the shore of Hudson Bay. Were it not for the gentle influence of the Gulf Stream carrying warm water across the Atlantic to western Europe, the sea around Britain, and particularly the North Sea, would be frozen solid in midwinter. As things are, the peculiarities of climate give Scotland, as far north as it is, a much less severe winter than is typical in Canada, but it is also much rarer for the Scots to have a hot summer. In fact, in Glasgow, where I was born, I doubt very much that the temperature has *ever* gone as low as zero degrees Fahrenheit, while in Edinburgh if the temperature ever exceeds about seventy degrees Fahrenheit most residents begin to wonder if the end of the world is at hand. However, in fairness to the land of my birth, I should perhaps mention that a Professor of Physics in London said that the North Americans had cleverly concealed from the rest of the world that their country was quite uninhabitable! Be that as it may, the Lowlands of Scotland where Maxwell was born and bred are perfectly habitable, but I suspect that the always uncertain climate—although rarely extreme—plays a part in producing a race of men who are suspicious of displays of emotion or exuberance, skeptical, and hard to convince—in brief, "canny" Scots. Perhaps in many ways this is a good foundation for being a scientist of one kind or another. Indeed, Scotland has produced proportionately an ample share of scientists and engineers in terms of its rather meager population of a few millions.

Two Scottish families were intermingled in Maxwell's ancestory—the Clerks and the Maxwells. Maxwell's paternal grandfather was a Captain James Clerk, a sea captain in the service of the Honourable East India Company, which in those days was responsible for Britain's trade and authority in India. Through the death of an older brother of this Captain Clerk, by name Sir John Clerk (Baronet) of Penicuik (now almost a suburb of Edinburgh), two estates came down to Captain Clerk's sons. The older son inherited the baronetcy, becoming Sir George Clerk, Bart., of Penicuik, while the younger son, John, got the lesser estate of Middlebie, in southern Scotland, but inherited no title. Since Middlebie had originally come into the Clerk family from the Maxwell family, this younger son of Captain Clerk also added the surname Maxwell on inheriting Middlebie, so becoming John Clerk Maxwell. Finally, this John Clerk Maxwell in turn was the father of James Clerk Maxwell. A Scottish friend of mine who has lived much of his life in the countryside around Edinburgh tells me that this business of taking on a second surname when inheriting some land is really quite a common occurrence in well-to-do Scottish families. If it had not been for the estate of Middlebie, we would now have been writing instead about a man named James Clerk, and it would have been "Clerk's equations" that would now be famous throughout the world rather than "Maxwell's equations." From this point on when we refer to anyone baldly as "Maxwell," it will always mean James Clerk Maxwell.

We are told that when Maxwell's father, John Clerk Maxwell, first acquired the Middlebie estate he was not very interested in it and spent his time in the city of Edinburgh. Although a lawyer by profession, he was particularly keen on attending meetings of the Royal Society of Edinburgh, of which more later. After John

Clerk Maxwell married, however, he apparently became more interested in the possibilities of country life; the birth of his son James probably reinforced this interest. Even today many confirmed urban bachelors or spinsters set about acquiring a house outside the city when they get married and think of raising a family. Mr. and Mrs. John Clerk Maxwell did just this, and a house, by name "Glenlair," was built on the Middlebie estate. The house lies near the village of Nether Corsock, close to the Water of Urr. (This rather romantic way of naming small rivers or streams is not uncommon in Scotland: for example, the so-called Water of Leith runs through parts of Edinburgh itself.) The church parish around the Middlebie estate was called Parton, and the village of Parton itself lies about three miles as the crow flies from the village of Corsock. Corsock Church was built only a mile or two from the Maxwell house, and Maxwell's body was brought for burial to Corsock Churchyard after his death in Cambridge in 1879.

When I was thinking about writing this book, my father made a visit to the Maxwell countryside, which is in the part of Scotland known as Kirkcudbrightshire and close to the boundary of Dumfriesshire; in particular he visited "Glenlair" and Corsock Church, and both he and the Registrar there, Mr. Sam Callander, took some photographs for me. The interior of Glenlair was burned out some years ago, but Plate 16 shows the house as it is today, Plate 17 shows Corsock Church, Plate 18a shows Maxwell's grave in the churchyard, and Plate 18b and c, taken inside the church, show the memorial window and memorial plate to Maxwell's memory.

Although Maxwell was born in Edinburgh, much of his early boyhood was spent on the Middlebie estate at Glenlair. His mother writes charmingly about him when he was scarcely three years old: "He is a very happy man, and has improved much since the weather got moderate;* he has great work with doors, locks, keys, etc., and 'Show me how it doos'† is never out of his mouth. He also investigates the hidden course of streams and bellwires, the way the water gets from the pond through the wall . . . and down a drain into Water Orr. . . . As to the bells, they will not rust; he stands sentry in the kitchen . . . or he rings, and sends Bessy to see and shout to let him know, and he drags papa all over to show him the holes where the wires go through." For a child less than three years old this persistent interest in the precise operation of things about him is remarkable, and suggests at least that a very determined mind was in the making. I might mention that in older British houses one often finds high up on the kitchen wall a collection of bells which were used for summoning servants to various rooms in the house, the bells being operated by wires running through tubes and so on through the walls of the house. When the wires had to go around corners, a little hinge of sorts was used, known naturally enough as a "bell crank." This name prevails today in various fields of

* The usage of "man" (or perhaps more commonly "wee man") to refer to a small boy is quite common in Scotland to this day. I sometimes wonder what to make of the opposite custom in North America of referring to adult men and women as "boys" and "girls." One might also remark that it is *always* a happy event in Scotland when and if "the weather gets moderate."

† The spelling of "doos" (for "does") and "Orr" (for "Urr") are as they appear in this letter dated April 25, 1834, written by Mrs. John Clerk Maxwell from Corsock to a sister-in-law of her husband. The letter is reproduced in *The Life of James Clerk Maxwell* by L. Campbell and W. Garnett (Macmillan & Co., Ltd., London, 1882). We shall refer in the future to this comprehensive life of Maxwell as Campbell and Garnett.

engineering when rods have to operate around corners —for example, when moving switches on railroads.

Another childhood phrase constantly used by Maxwell was: "What's the go of that?" and his perseverance in finding out the specific details of operation of some device or part of nature around him is also reflected in his next question. For if he was not satisfied with the first explanation of something or other, he would ask again: "But what is the *particular* go of that?" His father seems to have been fascinated above all with mechanical and scientific questions, and James Clerk Maxwell must have been a most rewarding and delightful son for him to bring up.

As a boy of twelve or thirteen I was rather scared of my father as a disciplinarian (I don't think he often had to say No twice), but I think some of my happiest times in those days were when my father explained the mysteries of alternating current as we traveled on railway trains from Glasgow to Edinburgh. I wanted to use electrical transformers on my model railway system, and it seemed so beautifully clear when my father explained their operation that I was rather surprised years later at the University to find that much more had to be said in lectures about the basic theory.

EDUCATION

When Maxwell was ten, his father decided he should go to a school in Edinburgh, and he chose the Edinburgh Academy. Maxwell remained a pupil at Edinburgh Academy until the age of sixteen, when he went to Edinburgh University. I have this much in common with Maxwell (but sadly little more), that we both went to Edinburgh Academy and to Edinburgh University. I am afraid I was far from popular at the Academy, and I think I take some comfort now to find that Maxwell, too, had rather a rough time of it at first; his nickname at school was "Daftie." I never enjoyed Edinburgh Academy much as a boy, nor to be honest do I think the Academy enjoyed me, but Maxwell seems to have become quite fond of his old school in later years. He wrote a poem in praise of the Academy, of which the chorus runs:

> "Dear old Academy!
> Queer old Academy.
> A merry lot were we, I wot,
> When at our old Academy."

Mind you, it is very common for older people to become sentimental about their school days, and to talk glibly about "the happiest days of my life." When I was at Edinburgh Academy, it often seemed to me that it was regarded by many as more important to be in the first team for rugby football than to be good at mathematics or the like, which was all I had to offer, and certainly I do not remember anyone's ever telling *me* as a schoolboy that the most distinguished pupil they had ever had there was James Clerk Maxwell. However, the *Edinburgh Academy Chronicle* for June and July 1931 (the centenary of Maxwell's birth) carries an article about him, and the whole of the poem I mentioned above is reproduced. Yet even at that late date the *Chronicle* still seems to me to have been a bit doubtful about Maxwell's greatness. Toward the close of the article the question is asked: "Now, was Maxwell a very great man—or only a great man?" For someone who probably ranks next to Newton in science throughout the whole world this seems a rather skeptical question. And the last sentences of the memorial article are to me even more confounding: "And it is of the work of an Academy boy that he is speaking. Surely we are right to be proud of him." I may be quite wrong, and quite unfair to this old school, but the apparent condescension of that remark still leaves me aghast.

One of Maxwell's contemporaries at the Academy, who was born in the same year (1831), was Peter Guthrie Tait who, after going to Cambridge University as did Maxwell, ultimately became Professor of Physics (or Natural Philosophy, as it is called in Scotland) at Edinburgh University. Thomson (Lord Kelvin) and P. G. Tait together wrote what became in those days a famous textbook of physics, and as a pair they were known affectionately as "T" (Thomson) and "T′" (Tait).[1] Now one of the most satisfying things, I think, about belonging to the scientific profession is the constant exchange of ideas, and the pleasure one gets in writing letters to one another on problems of common interest. Perhaps this very agreeable custom is less common today because of the general hurry and bustle, and also because there are so many scientific journals nowadays in which so many papers can be published. Thus maybe physicists, mathematicians, or chemists feel that there is not the same need to write letters to one another. I suppose also that the telephone and the jet plane eliminate much of the need for letters, but I myself am still rather old-fashioned, and enjoy very much writing to, and receiving letters from, other physicists who can be persuaded to correspond with me. At least this addiction of mine is in a good tradition, for while Maxwell was Professor of Physics at Aberdeen he wrote often to Tait. These letters are signed either J. C. Maxwell or simply J.C.M., and nothing very odd about *that*. However, like the little private joke about William Thomson and P. G. Tait referring to themselves as "T" and "T′", Maxwell frequently signed himself "dp/dt" (see Plate 19 where we have reproduced a postcard written by Maxwell to Thomson in Glasgow). The private joke here arises because a relation in thermodynamics (and thermodynamics was of great interest to both Maxwell and Kelvin) could be written[2] in the form dp/dt = JCM. You will see in Plate 20 that this symbolic signature is also recorded on the bust of Maxwell at Aberdeen University. Perhaps the wise-cracking humor of today may make us a little contemptuous of jokes like that. Whatever we may think, this kind of private joke peculiar to one profession or another has gone on for quite a long time—musical composers, I am told, have been prone to musical "puns," and to the making up of tunes based on some fellow composer's initials. Moreover, although it might have been an unwise assessment to make, I am sure that neither Maxwell nor Thomson (and certainly not Faraday) would have objected much to being regarded as quite unsophisticated outside their profession, and indeed their biographers are often at pains to point out that these men were quite simple and straightforward human beings. So, for example, Maxwell's obituary in *Nature* (issue of November 13, 1879) remarks: "He took great interest in passing events, though he never indulged in political discussions. . . . Though he never entered into theological controversy, . . . his simple Christian faith gave him a peace too deep to be ruffled by bodily pain or external circumstances. . . ." And of Lord Kelvin in later life it was said: "Wealthy and famous and of prodigious learning, he is still one of the most modest and simple-minded of men, with an exquisitely gentle face framed in snow-white hair, and a smile which is like a benediction. . . ."

As a matter of fact, it appears that in the last century scientists as a group were held in rather high esteem; when William Thomson at the age of sixty-eight was made a Peer, becoming Lord Kelvin, one finds it written that: "Not for services connected with the destruction of human life but for those that elevate its character, enlarge its capacities, and increase its happiness, the new Peer has his honour." This sort of thing, it seems to me, is (happily) rather far from the present-day popular image of scientists as depicted in horror movies, strip cartoons, and the like. Today they seem to correspond in many people's minds more to Stevenson's Mr. Hyde than to Dr. Jekyll, as dangerous men bent on the destruction of the world, or perhaps at best they are thought of as rather bungling, absent-minded souls who dabble about in ivory towers.

Maxwell's First Scientific Paper

While James Clerk Maxwell was still at Edinburgh Academy he wrote a paper on "Oval Curves," and a summary of his paper was published in the *Proceedings of the Royal Society of Edinburgh,* in April 1846, when he was still only fourteen years old. In Plate 21 are reproduced the first few pages of Maxwell's original manuscript, which is in the hands of the Royal Society of Edinburgh. Actually, Maxwell's paper was read to the Society by a Professor Forbes, because it was thought somewhat undignified in those days for a mere schoolboy to be allowed to address directly the members of the Society. The idea behind Maxwell's paper on oval curves was a pretty one.

It is well known that if you stick two pins into a board, fasten a loose loop of cotton around the pins, and then trace out a curve with the point of a pencil holding the loop tautly at all times, you will end up with an ellipse. The figure on page 65 shows an ellipse drawn in just this way. This procedure works because an ellipse can be defined as a curve drawn so that the sum of the distances from any point on the curve to two fixed points is a constant. (The two fixed points are

[14] *James Clerk Maxwell (1831–79).*

[15] a. (top) A closeup of the memorial plaque on the outside wall of the house where Maxwell was born. b. (bottom) Maxwell's birthplace in India Street, Edinburgh.

[16] *The Maxwells' house, "Glenlair," as it stands today.*

[17] *Corsock Church, Scotland, in whose churchyard James Clerk Maxwell was buried.*

[18] *a. (top left) Tombstone of James Clerk Maxwell in Corsock Churchyard. The stone also records the deaths of his father, his mother, and his wife. b. (top right) Stained glass memorial window to the memory of James Clerk Maxwell, in Corsock Church. c. (bottom) Memorial Plate to Maxwell, inside Corsock Church:*

"To the Memory of
James Clerk Maxwell
*Born 13 June 1831 * Died 5 November 1879*
of Glenlair a Faithful Elder of this Church
First Professor of Experimental Physics
in the University of Cambridge

This window is erected by admirers of a genius
that discovered the kinship between electricity
and light and was led through the mystery of
nature to the fuller knowledge of God."

[19] *Postcard sent by Maxwell (signed "dp/dt") to William Thomson in 1872. On the front of the postcard Thomson in 1899 (by then Lord Kelvin) noted that it should be preserved.*

JAMES CLERK
MAXWELL
PROFESSOR OF NATURAL PHILOSOPHY
1856-1860

[20] *Bust of James Clerk Maxwell in the University of Aberdeen. The symbol on the left below the bust refers to the planet Saturn, and Maxwell's analysis of the constitution of Saturn's rings. The symbol on the right, "dp/dt," was the form of signature Maxwell used often in his scientific correspondence (as discussed in the text).*

Observations on circumscribed figures having a plurality of foci, and radii of various proportions—
by James Clerk Maxwell.

Some time ago while considering the analogy of the Circle and Ellipsis—and the common method of drawing the latter figure by means of a cord of any given length—fixed by the ends to the foci; which rests on the principle, that the sum of the two lines drawn from the foci to any point in the circumference is a constant quantity; it occurred to me that the sum of the Radii being constant—was the essential condition in all circumscribed figures, and that the foci may be of any number and the radii of various proportions.—

This rule applies to the circle—here there is one focus & one length of radius—In the Ellipsis, there are two foci—& to any point of the circumference two radii—the sum of which are constant—and the circle may be considered as drawn on the same principle supposing the two foci & radii to be conjoined

Impressed with these views, I proceeded to put them

to the practical test of tracing figures on the principle of
the constant quantity of the radii — of various proportions —

The most simple proportion of one to two was first tried
with two foci — which I did nearly by doubling the thread
which was attached to one of the foci — A & B are the two foci.

A thread is fixed on the focus B at the other end is loop at D for the
tracing point and the thread is passed round a pin in the focus A — the
tracing point is then carried round the figure guided by the bight of
the thread as shown by the red line — by this arrangement the
elliptical figure is modified by the preponderating influence of
the double proportion of the Radius A D. which enlarges that end
of the figure and a fine Oval form is produced — The propor=

-tions of a figure produced in this way are affected by the distance between the foci. The method I have adopted for giving a measure for fixing that distance is to state the Angle at one of the foci B formed by the lines to the other focus & to a point in the circumference C. the line A. C. being always drawn straight angle to the Axis A B. in this figure it is about 25°—

This figure may be defined. either to be a figure with two foci in which the sum, of one of the radii and twice the sum of the other is a constant quantity. or it may be regarded as a figure of three foci — two of them being coincident, and the sum of the three radii constant — as the circle may be said to be of any number of foci all coincident — for if in the figure, A & B— were made to coincide then a circle would be traced with a triple radius—

Having thus obtained the Oval form — I proceeded to draw it with the distances of the foci varied — On a separate paper are a series of examples — It is obvious that if the distance of the foci is very small, The figure will differ but little from the circle — The first of the series is marked as drawn on an angle of 15° as explained above — then 30°— 27°— 24°— at this angle the focus of the triple radius is in the circumference & the figure is of a pointed form —

(4)   the focus is out of the figure &

at lower angles, the small end again becomes more rounded

as seen by the example of 22°. 30' — & 18° — in the last example

the focus is supposed at an infinite distance — exposed by the

parallel lines, in which case, the figure is still of oval form — but

the difference in the two ends is infinitely small —

Having investigated the varieties of form producible for the two foci

with the radii — as one & two — I have drawn figures with the

proportion of 1 to 3 — 1 to 4 — 2 to 3 — 3 to 4 — all done by

lapping the tracing thread so many times round the pins

placed in the foci — The greater the difference in the proportion

such as 1 to 3 the figure of the oval next the preponderating focus

approaches more nearly to the circle — and the less the difference

between the power of the foci as in the case the radii being as 3 to 4 —

the form is kept more nearly to the ellipsis — and by adjusting

the distances between the foci — innumerable varieties of the

oval form can be produced — but I have not had leisure

to draw many examples — but a few are drawn on a separate

paper —

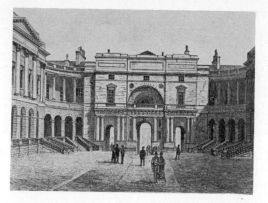

[22] *Reproduction of a print from Grant's* Old and New Edinburgh, *Vol. 3, showing the court of The Old Quadrangle at Edinburgh University as it was in Maxwell's day as a student there.*

Nº	Mark	Name	1847-8 Country	Address in Edinʳ	Age	Day
1	77	James Craig	Kinross	7 East Register St	2½	12
2	167	James Cowie	Stirling	30 East Grey St	2	J.
3	171	Kenneth Mackay	Rosshire	9 Wemyss Pl⁰	2	J.
4	122	William Walker	St Petersburg	24 Dublin St	1-2	J.
5	127	Patrick S. Fraser	Kinross	16 Drull College St	3	J.
6	558	Edward B. Bachman	Edinburgh	14 Duke Street	2	J.
7	86	David Sandeman	Perth	3 Dewar Place	2	J.
8	92	James Clerk Maxwell	Kirkcudbright	31 Heriot Row	2	J.
9	66	John Haldane	Leith	2 London Row	1-2	J.
10	158	James Islmosta	Tranent	55 Cumberland St	2	J.
11	220	George Fyfe	Edinburgh	India Bank Dom	5½	
12	165	R. G. Donaldson, Felly	Northumberland		2	J.
13	180	Robert Duke	Sligo	9 Randolph Place		
14	103	David Whitelaw	Edinburgh	28 Mess Register St	2+	J.
15	243	Robert Macfarlane	Stirlingshire	Greenhill, Falkirk	2	J.
16	175	Alexander Brunton	Edinburgh	27 N. Richmond St	2	J.
17	276	Peter Guthrie Tait	Midlothian	Somerset Cottage	—	—
18	106	Allan Stewart	Perth	20 Great King Street	1-2	J.
19	198	George Pringle	Roxburgh	14 Albany St	1-2	13

[23] *Mathematical Class List of students at Edinburgh University for the Academic Year 1847–48 showing Maxwell's name (no. 8) and that of P. G. Tait (no. 17).*

[24] *The planet Saturn as photographed at Lick Observatory through a 36-inch refracting telescope. Maxwell made a very full theoretical study of the rings of Saturn and was awarded the Adams Prize of Cambridge University for this work.*

[25] *The signature of James Clerk Maxwell on April 21, 1856 in the Roll Book of Fellows of the Royal Society of Edinburgh after his election.*

Albemarle St London W
13 Novr 1857

My dear Sir

Upon a former occasion, I ventured to ask you what your thoughts of my papers, it was very wrong; for I do not think anyone should be called upon for the expression of their thoughts before they are prepared, and wish, to give them. I have often enough to decline giving an opinion because my mind is not ready to come to a conclusion, or does not wish to be committed to a view, that may by further consideration be changed. But having received your last letter, I am exceedingly grateful to you for it; and rejoice that my forgetfulness of having sent the former paper on conservation, has brought about such a result. Your letter is to me the first intercommunication on the subject with one of your mode & habit of thinking. It will do me much good; and I shall read and meditate it again & again.

I dare say I have myself greatly to blame for the vague use of expressive words. I perceive that I do not use the word "force" as you define it "the tendency of a body to pass from one place to another" What I mean by the word is the source or sources of all possible actions of the particles or materials of the universe: these being often called the powers of nature, when spoken of in respect of the different manners in which their effects are shewn. In a paper which I have received at the moment from the Phil. Mag. by Sr. W. Snow they are called the "forces such as electricity heat &c." In this way I have used the word "force" in the description of gravity which I have given as that expressing the received idea of its nature & source; and such of my remarks as express an opinion or are critical, apply only to that sense of it. You may remember I speak to labourers like myself, experimentalists on force generally, who receive that description of gravity as a physical truth and believe that it expresses all, and no more than all, that concerns the nature and locality of the power. To these it limits the formation of their ideas and the direction of their exertions, and to these I have endeavoured to speak; shewing how such a thought, if accepted, pledged them to a very limited and, probably, erroneous view of the cause of the force, and to ask them to consider, whether they should not look (for a time at least,) to a source in part external to the particles. I send you two or three old printed lines marked relating to this point. To those who disown the definition or description as imperfect, I have nothing to urge; as there is there probably no real difference between it.

I hang on to your words because they are to me weighty; and where you say "for my "part cannot realize your dissatisfaction with "the law of gravitation provided you conceive "it according to your own principles" they give me great comfort. I have nothing to say against the law of the action of gravity. It is against the law which measures its total strength as an inherent force that I venture to oppose my opinion; and I must have expressed myself badly (though I don't find the weak point) or I should not have conveyed any other impression. All I wanted to do was to move men (not N⁰ 1 but N⁰ 11.) from the unreserved acceptance of a principle of physical action which might be opposed to natural truth. The idea that we may possibly have to connect repulsion with the lines of gravitation force (which is going far beyond anything my mind would venture on at present except in private cogitation) shews how far we may have to depart from the view I oppose.

There is one thing I would be glad to ask you. When a mathematician engaged in investigating physical actions and results has arrived at his conclusions, may they not be expressed in common language as fully, clearly, and definitely as in ma

mathematical formulæ? If so would it
not be a great boon to such as I to express them so?—translating them out of their
hieroglyphics, that we also might work
upon them by experiment. I think it
must be so, because I have always
found that you could convey to me a
perfectly clear idea of your conclusions;
which, though they may give me no full
understanding of the steps of your process, give me the results neither above
nor below the truth;—and so clear in
character that I can think and work
from them. If this be possible would it
not be a good thing if mathematicians,
working on these subjects, were to give us
the results in this popular, useful, working
state, as well as in that which is their
own and proper to them

Ever My dear Sir
Most truly Yours
M Faraday

Professor
J. C. Maxwell Esqre
&c &c &c

[27] Letter dated February 13, 1871 from the Rev. E. W. Blore, M.A. (later Vice-Master of Trinity College, Cambridge) inviting Maxwell to become a candidate for the Cavendish Professorship at Cambridge.

[28] *Dynamical adjustable top by Maxwell.*

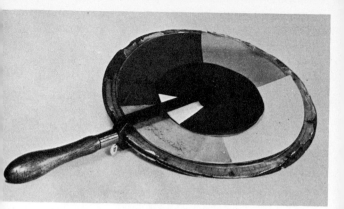

[29] *Colored disc apparatus by Maxwell.*

[30] *Spinning coil apparatus; Maxwell hoped to detect inertial effects of electric current with this.*

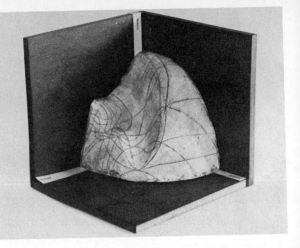

[31] *Model of "thermodynamic surface" of water constructed by Maxwell, following the work of Josiah Willard Gibbs.*

Gentlemen at Practical Work
Last Term 1877

Mr. Chrystal   Corpus.
"   Schuster
"   Shaw   Emmanuel
"   Ohm   Do
"   Sharratt   Do
"   Hargreaves   St. Johns
"   ...hook   Trinity
                      Kings

[32] *Fragment of record (in Maxwell's handwriting) of students working in the Cavendish Laboratory during Maxwell's tenure there as Professor.*

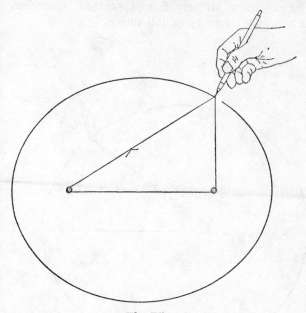

The Ellipse

called the "foci" of the ellipse.) By having a fixed length of cotton and moving the pencil around so that the loop is kept taut, we automatically ensure that the condition defining the ellipse is fulfilled. Now Maxwell had the idea of *generalizing* this sort of technique, and he thought about curves where, for example, the sum of the distance from one focus plus *three* times the distance from the other focus is to remain constant. We can now arrange for this requirement by winding our loop of cotton back around one of the foci before we complete the loop, and the figure on page 66 shows the asymmetrical smooth egg-shaped curve that we obtain. The Latin for egg is "ovum," so this general family of curves may be called ovoid curves, and James Clerk

Maxwell wrote his very first paper (and, remember, he was only fourteen) on this subject.

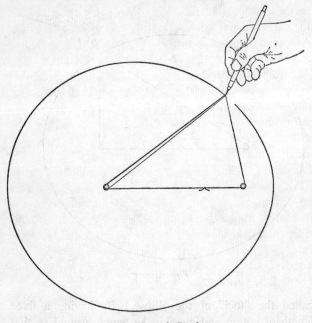

The Ovoid Circle

This possibility of *generalizing* a scientific procedure, a principle, or for that matter something immediately practical, is surely one of the vital factors in real invention. There is the well-known, but usually garbled, story about Isaac Newton that he saw an apple fall, and so in a flash discovered gravity! Nowadays it is quite common to suggest that the whole story is mythical, but actually Newton himself talked about the experience in his later years. One could hardly say that Newton "discovered" gravity (people had already assumed that the earth attracted objects such as apples or human beings to it), but Newton made the brilliant generalization that perhaps the *same* force that attracted apples to the earth was *also* attracting the moon to the earth, so keeping the moon in its orbit around the earth when it might otherwise just fly off into space. A young friend of Newton, by name Stukeley, told of a conversation he had with Newton in his latter days. According to Stukeley: "After dinner, the weather being warm, we went into the garden and drank thea [sic], under the shade of some apple trees, only he and myself. Amidst other discourse, he told me, he was just in the same situation as when formerly the notion of gravitation came into his mind. It was occasion'd by the fall of an apple, as he sat in a contemplative mood . . ." and Stukeley continued: "And thus by degrees he began to apply this property of gravitation to the motion of the earth and of the heavenly bodys, to consider their distances, their magnitudes and their periodical revolutions. . . ." Newton himself described his discovery in this way: "In the same year [that is, in 1666] I began to think of gravity extending to the orb of the moon and . . . I deduced that the forces which keep the planets in their orbs must be reciprocally as the squares of their distances from the centres about which they revolve: and thereby compared the force requisite to keep the moon in her orb with the force of gravity at the surface of the earth, and found them answer pretty nearly. . . ."

I would say that Benjamin Franklin made another superb generalization when he established that lightning was just the same sort of stuff as the small electrical sparks one could make in a laboratory in those days, or in North America by simply combing one's hair in the dark on any dry winter's evening. And certainly Faraday's concept of electric and magnetic lines of force, originally derived from observing the behavior of iron filings near a magnet, was a very powerful and fruitful generalization. One should also realize how many of the great advances in mathematics depend basically on some vital generalization of what has gone before. The very concepts of fractional or negative numbers are born from a generalization; for you may well have one, three, or ten cats, dogs, or horses, but after all ⅔ of a horse, or ⅝ of a cat, is quite a different matter; and only by a rather special interpretation of what is meant could you talk about "minus five horses." And in this vein, mathematicians for a very long time said simply that "the square root of minus one just does not exist."[3] The generalization of the idea of numbers to admit such concepts as $\sqrt{-1}$ to logical discussion and useful analysis was, I believe, one of the greatest intellectual achievements of man; the whole new field of so-called "complex numbers" which then emerged has been enormously profitable and valuable both in pure and applied mathematics. Now hindsight is of course always rather easy, but surely Maxwell's very early determination to understand *precisely* how things around him worked (such as the house bells at Glenlair), his determination not to be fobbed off without unearthing a detailed explanation ("But what is the *particular* go of that?"), together with this equally vital capacity for generalizing, show very clearly his early potentialities as a first-class scientist.

We shall see later that William Thomson, the future Lord Kelvin, was already attending his father's lectures at Glasgow University at the precocious age of eight, but Maxwell did not go to Edinburgh University until he was about sixteen years old; he continued there as a student for some three years, from 1847 to 1850 (Plates 22 and 23). Thereafter he went to Peterhouse (known then as St. Peter's College) at the University of Cambridge.[4]

The tradition of going at a rather young age to study at a university in Scotland still holds good today. It was certainly nothing remarkable that I myself had just turned seventeen when I went to Edinburgh University to study Mathematics and Natural Philosophy (Physics); indeed, another student in the same year was only sixteen and a half at that time. Our English neighbors are usually about nineteen when first they go to universities such as Oxford and Cambridge, but then a Scotsman may well wonder whether the English do not take rather longer to mature. To be fair, though, it is true that in the days of Maxwell and Thomson the standards of education for undergraduates in such things as mathematics were considerably higher in Cambridge University than in the Scottish universities. And it is still quite common today for Scottish students who come out "on top" to go on to Cambridge University for further scientific training, just as Maxwell, Thomson, and P. G. Tait all did in their time.

The great distinction for a mathematician in those days particularly was to come out at the head of the Final Honours Examination in Cambridge, which is known as the "Mathematics Tripos." Until recently the names of the successful candidates in the Mathematics Tripos were published by the University in order of merit, the top man being known as Senior Wrangler, the coveted distinction. Neither Maxwell nor Thomson became Senior Wrangler, although each in his year was placed second in order of merit. However, in their turn both Maxwell and Thomson won the Smith's Prize. The examination for this prize followed immediately after the Mathematics Tripos Examination, and was apparently regarded as a greater test of real mathematical power and originality of thought than the Tripos examination itself. Maxwell actually shared the Smith's Prize with a famous dynamicist, by name Routh,[5] who was Senior Wrangler in that year.

Neither Thomson at Glasgow, nor Maxwell at Edinburgh, seems to have completed the requirements for official graduation at the Scottish universities, probably because (as we are told in Thomson's case) this might have adversely influenced their undergraduate status at Cambridge University. Perhaps I may say, somewhat wryly, that Oxford and Cambridge appear to look after this kind of situation quite simply today by just not recognizing (*officially*) the degrees of any other universities in the official but their own and those of Trinity College, Dublin. While he was at Edinburgh University, Maxwell keenly studied Mathematics, some Natural Philosophy and Chemistry, and also Philosophy. It is another tradition of the Scottish universities, which still holds good today, that even those students specializing in one particular field such as Modern Languages or Physical Science, must nonetheless spend some time on "outside subjects" (i.e., outside their field of specialization). Philosophy is a very popular choice as an outside subject for those specializing in Mathematics and Physical Science. I remember seeing the names of Medallists year by year in one of the Philosophy courses painted up on the walls of a classroom at Edinburgh University, and I also believe I remember seeing among these names that of a "J. C. Maxwell." I have tried unsuccessfully to find out whether that J. C. Maxwell was in fact James Clerk Maxwell, but in any case Clerk Maxwell was certainly a very keen student of Philosophy. Campbell and Garnett tell us that: "The lectures in Mental Philosophy . . . interested him greatly. . . . Though only sixteen when he entered the Logic Class, he worked hard for it, . . . and from the Class of Metaphysics, . . . his mind gained many lasting impressions. His boundless curiosity was fed by the Professor's inexhaustible learning; . . . while his mystical tendency was soothed by the distinction between Knowledge and Belief. . . ." By the way, as evidence that traditions die hard in Scotland, the first-year class in Philosophy is known even today as the class of Logic and Metaphysics.

In those years in Edinburgh Maxwell published two more papers in the *Transactions of the Royal Society of Edinburgh,* one on the theory of Rolling Curves, which was read to the Society in February 1849, when Maxwell was seventeen, and a year later a very lengthy paper on Elastic Solids. The first of these papers was read to the Society by Professor Kelland, apparently because it was thought that Maxwell was still too young to speak directly to the Society. According to Campbell and Garnett: ". . . it was not thought appropriate for a boy in a round jacket to mount the rostrum there." However, Maxwell seems to have delivered his paper on Elastic Solids himself.

The greatest difficulty in trying to tell the story of a man such as Maxwell in a brief essay is the tremendous breadth of his work. Probably William Thomson, Lord Kelvin, is an even more difficult subject from this point of view because one could say with justice that in his day there was hardly a field of physical science to which he did not contribute. But Maxwell lived only to the age of forty-eight, yet did top-flight work in dynamics, astrophysics, the problem of color vision, the kinetic theory of gases, in thermodynamics, and above all in electromagnetism! We must therefore skim very lightly over the whole spread of Maxwell's contributions, although the vast majority of physicists would be overjoyed if they could contribute work of this quality to any single field of research. That is the trouble with the really first-class mind . . . it seems to be able to tackle so many things well, and makes most of us, as possessors of second-class minds at best, feel pedestrian, and clumsy.

TEACHING AT CAMBRIDGE AND ABERDEEN

Though Maxwell first went to Cambridge University as an undergraduate at Peterhouse, before long he transferred to Trinity College. After completing the Mathematics Tripos Examination as Second Wrangler and sharing the Smith's Prize with Routh in 1854, Maxwell was elected to a Fellowship of Trinity College. To hold a Fellowship of a Cambridge or Oxford college has in the past been a rather agreeable occupation—particularly if the man was fortunate in having stimulating contemporaries and if the college had good kitchens and wine cellars. One of the main responsibilities was to supervise the studies of undergraduates in the particular field that the Fellow himself had specialized in. Today this remains true, but unfortunately the immense increase in the numbers of science students has placed a heavy burden of teaching on many College Fellows, and they are often left with too little time to study independently, and to think about their own field of work. And indeed this is now the common lot of university staffs in most countries.

Even today many College Fellows (usually known as dons) at Oxford or Cambridge prefer to remain where they are, rather than to accept offers of Chairs at some other university.[6] Why then did Maxwell (and also William Thomson) leave Cambridge and accept a Chair of Physics at a Scottish university at a rather early age? It seems that each man's father played an important part in the decision. William Thomson's father, Professor James Thomson of Glasgow University, was certainly most anxious that his son would get the Chair of Physics at Glasgow, and did all he could to ensure that this would happen. Maxwell felt that a Chair in Scotland would enable him to be close to his father and allow them to spend time together at their house (Glenlair) in the Border country. Maxwell also felt that the rather secluded college life at Cambridge might narrow his outlook and that it would be wise to go out into the world, at least for some time.

Professor Forbes of Edinburgh University (who had read Maxwell's first paper for him to the Royal Society of Edinburgh) told him that the Chair of Physics was vacant at Marischal College, Aberdeen. Maxwell's election to the Chair was announced in April 1856, when he was still only twenty-four years old, and it is sad that his father should have died but a few days earlier. Oddly enough, Thomson's father died (of cholera) very shortly after William Thomson was elected, at only twenty-two years of age, to the Chair of Natural Philosophy at Glasgow in 1846, just ten years before Maxwell's appointment in Aberdeen.

There seems little doubt that Maxwell was never a forceful lecturer, nor, for that matter, that he was ever very fond of lecturing—the two go naturally together. Perhaps the burden of lecturing contributed to Maxwell's somewhat jaundiced opinion of his fellow Scots at Aberdeen. He remarked at one time: "No jokes of any kind are understood here, I have not made one for two months and if I feel one coming I shall bite my tongue!" I remember myself some years ago thanking a senior lecturer at Oxford for a very lucid course of his that I had attended; whereupon he replied that if any credit was due, it was to his earlier students at a Scottish university who were so stupid that lecturers had to be blindingly clear if they were to be understood at all! Whether or not Scottish undergraduates are less quick-witted than their counterparts in Oxford or Cambridge, it is true that lectures have greater importance in the Scottish universities than in Oxford or Cambridge, and it also seems certain that Maxwell, unlike Faraday, was not particularly gifted in this direction. His stay in Aberdeen was not a long one, for in 1860 a union took place of the Colleges in Aberdeen,[7] forming Aberdeen University, and certain Professorships became redundant. Maxwell's Chair at Marischal College was one of these, and in the same year he accepted the Chair of Physics at King's College, London. His own comments on the selection of professors are rather caustic: Writing to Lewis Campbell (who later became his biographer) from Aberdeen, in December 1857, he said: "College Fusion is holding up its head again. . . . Know all men I am a Fusionist, and thereby an enemy of . . . Unionists ([those who wish to] unite the three learned faculties, and leave double chairs in Arts). But there is no use writing out their theory to you. They want inferior men for professors— men who will find it their interest to teach what will pay to small classes, and who will be more under the influence of parents and the local press than more learned or better paid men would be in a larger college. . . ." Again it seems that Maxwell's opinion of the Aberdonian powers-that-be was not very high!

THE RINGS OF SATURN

For Maxwell those early years at Aberdeen were most productive in research work, partly because he could spend a good bit of time quietly at Glenlair or elsewhere away from teaching responsibilities. In 1856 he had won the Adams Prize at Cambridge for a scientific paper, or "essay," dealing with the structure of the rings of the planet Saturn (Plate 24). This problem fascinated him; he continued to work at it during the next two or three years while he was Professor at

Aberdeen, and in 1859 he had a book published on the subject by the Cambridge University Press.

If one looks at the thin, disc-like, circular rings surrounding Saturn, the question arises whether they are solid, liquid, or gas, and how they retain their shape in a stable fashion as centuries go by. Maxwell's work to prove that the rings could be neither solid nor liquid in structure is noted in his own letters of this time. Writing again to Lewis Campbell (from Glenlair, on August 28, 1857), he said: ". . . I have been battering away at Saturn, returning to the charge every now and then. I have effected several breaches in the solid ring, and now I am splash into the fluid one, amid a clash of symbols truly astounding. When I reappear it will be in the dusky‡ ring, which is something like the state of the air supposing the siege of Sebastopol conducted from a forest of guns 100 miles one way, and 30,000 miles the other, and the shot never to stop, but go spinning away round a circle, radius 170,000 miles. . . ." And two months later, when writing to R. B. Litchfield, again from Glenlair, Maxwell says: ". . . I am grinding hard at Saturn and have picked many holes in him, and am fitting him up new and true. I am sure of most of him now, and have got over some stumbling-blocks which kept me niggling at calculations two years." And the following month, writing from Aberdeen to H. R. Droop: ". . . I am very busy with Saturn on the top of my regular work. He is all remodelled and recast, but I have more to do to him yet, . . ."

I think Einstein once said, more or less, that the

---

‡ The quotations are from Maxwell's letters as reproduced by Campbell and Garnett; and in this particular letter the word is "dusky" as reproduced there. Either Maxwell is using the word in the sense of "shadowy" (cf. *The Concise Oxford Dictionary*), or perhaps it is in error for "dusty."

only way to solve a problem was to work at it continuously and keep returning to it constantly, in other words to live with it. (Another remark by Einstein, somewhat related, runs as follows: "The only way to escape the personal corruption of praise is to go on working. One is tempted to stop and listen to it. The only thing is to turn away and go on working. Work. There is nothing else.") I suppose this is just another way of saying that "genius is an infinite capacity for taking pains," or that "inspiration is 90 per cent perspiration." Nonetheless, I think the other 10 per cent is vital because, unjust though it may be in this rough world of ours, hard work *alone* will not suffice to produce real creativity, but in any case Maxwell had *both* the inspiration, *and* the willingness to perspire! These typical letters of his show clearly his capacity to concentrate for long periods on a problem, so different from most of us, who find it hard to concentrate on anything, even a television show, for longer than an hour or so.

Kinetic Theory, Statistical Mechanics, and Color Vision

At this time Maxwell also had started to contribute to the immensely important field of work which we know as the kinetic theory of matter, and he presented his first paper on the kinetic theory of gases to the British Association in 1859. It was during the nineteenth century that the concept of matter as composed of billions upon billions of tiny atoms—each atom being characteristic of a given substance—became firmly established in physical science. When we sit in a quiet, closed room, we would say that on our everyday scale the air is "at rest"; unless we go around deliberately stirring things up, there appears to be no movement.

On the atomic scale, however, we have to think of every cubic inch of space around us as filled with about fifty billion billion (5×10^{19}) air molecules belting around at rather high speeds—somewhere between five hundred and a thousand miles per hour. On my desk there is a lump of copper about the size of a golf ball. It is made up of about a million billion billion (10^{24}) copper atoms, arranged for the most part in regular patterns like a military parade, but with each atom vibrating strongly, somewhat as if the soldiers on parade were swaying in the breeze. The whole basis of the atomic theory of matter is that the atoms or molecules which make up a block of ice, for example, or a glass of water, or steam coming from a kettle, remain essentially unchanged, but, simply, that their abundance and their freedom to move around are different in the three states of aggregation—solid, liquid, and gas.

To get the general idea of a theory, however, is one thing, and to be able to use it as a working principle of physical science is another; ideally, given a few facts such as the mass of a particular type of atom, and how many atoms we are concerned with, we wish to be able to predict in detail how a solid, liquid, or gas of that particular substance will behave—at what temperature it will melt, when it will boil, and so on. This still is a major field of physics today, and an important tool in the work is the discipline of statistical mechanics, which enables us to predict how billions and billions of atoms or molecules will behave together if we know a certain amount about the mechanics of a *single* atom or molecule. Maxwell and the great Austrian physicist Ludwig Boltzmann (1844–1906) laid much of the foundations of statistical mechanics with their theoretical studies of gases regarded as collections of vast numbers of gas molecules. If one has these billions upon billions of gas molecules constantly colliding with one another, obviously one will have to deal with a wide range of speeds; some molecules may have suffered severe collisions and consequently be going rather slowly, and others may have gained energy from such collisions and be traveling very fast. The statistical law describing the velocity range of gas molecules in a given system is known universally as the Maxwell-Boltzmann law of distribution of velocities, and we may say again that if Maxwell had done nothing else in his life but contribute to the discovery of this particular law, it would have been an adequate monument to his work.

Very closely allied to statistical mechanics and kinetic theory is the science of thermodynamics, which discusses how matter behaves in bulk when we vary the temperature, pressure, volume, and so on. Maxwell was keenly interested in this field, too, and we have in thermodynamics today four important relationships relating the behavior of thermodynamic parameters to one another; these equations are known as "Maxwell's thermodynamic relations" (one of these relations gave rise to Maxwell's "pen name," dp/dt; see p. 62 and Note 2). (See also Plate 31 showing a thermodynamic surface made by Maxwell himself.)

But this was not all. Maxwell in these years did original work in the theory of color vision and, above all, gave a great deal of thought to electromagnetism and Faraday's discoveries. On November 7, 1857, G. G. Stokes[8] wrote to Maxwell from the School of Mines in London: "I have just received your . . . account of experiments on the perception of colour. The latter, which I missed seeing at the time when it was published, I have just read with great interest. The results afford most remarkable and important evidence in favour of the theory of three primary colour-perceptions, a theory which you, and you alone, so far as I know, have established on an exact numerical basis." On the same day John Tyndall also wrote to Maxwell, saying: "I am very much obliged to you for your kind thoughtfulness in sending me your papers on the Dynamical Top and on the Perception of Colour, as also for your memoir on Lines of Force, received some time ago. I never doubted the possibility of giving Faraday's notions a mathematical form, and you would probably be one of the last to deny the possibility of a totally different imagery by which the phenomena might be represented."

Letters were also exchanged between Maxwell and Faraday. Faraday wrote a lengthy letter to Maxwell from the Royal Institution on November 13, 1857, discussing Maxwell's comments on Faraday's interpretation of electromagnetic behavior. It is clear from this that Faraday had an extremely high opinion of Maxwell's ability and perception as a physicist, and I feel that some theoreticians today might do well to reread what Faraday had to say: ". . . There is one thing I would be glad to ask you. When a mathematician engaged in investigating physical actions and results has arrived at his conclusions, may they not be expressed in common language as fully, clearly, and definitely as in mathematical formulae? If so, would it not be a great boon to such as I to express them so?—translating them out of their hieroglyphics, that we also might work upon them by experiment. I think it must be so, because I have always found that you could convey to me a perfectly clear idea of your conclusions, which, though they may give me no full understanding of the steps of your process, give me the results neither above nor below the truth, and so clear in character that I can think and work from them. If this be possible, would it not be a good thing if mathematicians, working on these subjects, were to give us the results in this popular, useful, working state, as well as in that which is their own and proper to them? Ever My dear Sir, Most truly yours, M. Faraday. To Professor J. C. Maxwell, Esq." This letter from Faraday to Maxwell is reproduced in Plate 26. It is fine to see the evident respect which Faraday, then sixty-six years of age, showed for Maxwell's ability—and bear in mind that Maxwell himself was only twenty-six years old when this letter was written to him!

While both Faraday and Thomson (as we shall see) in their long spans of life had so many honors offered and bestowed on them, Maxwell received but two honorary degrees—doctorates of law from Edinburgh University (1872) and from Oxford University (1876). He was, however, elected to Fellowship of the Royal Society of Edinburgh (Plate 25) when he was only twenty-four years old, and to Fellowship of the Royal Society of London on June 6, 1861, at the age of twenty-nine. He received the Rumford Medal of the Royal Society of London in 1860, and gave the Bakerian Lecture (a signal honor) in 1866 when still in his early thirties. After his period as professor at Aberdeen, Maxwell carried on his work as Professor of Physics at King's College, London, for about five years. There was then a period when he "retired" from active university life, until in 1871 he accepted the appointment as first Professor of Experimental Physics in Cambridge, and it was under his direction that the plans of the Cavendish Laboratory were prepared. He held this appointment until his death in Cambridge in 1879, at the rather early age of forty-eight.

THE ELECTROMAGNETIC THEORY AND
MAXWELL'S EQUATIONS

After the move from Aberdeen, his investigations continued unabated, particularly on the kinetic theory of gases, and there is a story that in London his wife (the former Katherine Mary Dewar, daughter of the Principal of Marischal College at Aberdeen) stoked the fire in the basement of their house so that he might carry on experiments on the thermal behavior of gases in the attic. So, at least in this respect, Mrs. Maxwell must have been of help to her husband, even if she dealt with him rather critically at times (see also p. 22). But Maxwell's final, and by far his greatest, achievement was his Electromagnetic Theory. As Faraday's work witnesses, the earlier years of the nineteenth century fairly bristled with exciting discoveries of one kind and another in electromagnetism. When once steady electric currents could be provided, Hans Oersted showed that a current flowing in a conductor produced magnetic effects just like the effects of a permanent magnet. Therefore, since two separate currents should behave like two magnets, and we know that magnets can attract or repel one another strongly, it followed, as indeed the experiments of Ampère and others showed, that there should be attractive or repulsive forces between two electric currents. Before long the laws of attraction and repulsion could be stated with the same *precision* Newton had been able to give to the law of gravitational attraction between any two particles of matter. Then came Faraday and Henry, who linked magnetism and electricity again through the beautiful discovery of electromagnetic induction.

And so it went on in a most exciting manner. Practical applications began to develop in the new technology of electromagnetism. An electric telegraph had achieved by 1840 the macabre distinction of apprehending a murderer; Atlantic cables were first laid in 1864 and 1866 (and in this achievement Lord Kelvin, whom we meet in the next chapter, played a great part); and Alexander Graham Bell obtained patents for the telephone in 1876 and 1877. But from the point of view of a sound scientific understanding, what was needed was some really adequate unified theory of electric and magnetic behavior so that one could predict in some very general way what would happen electromagnetically in space and time under any particular experimental conditions that might be envisaged. This is really what Maxwell's electromagnetic theory ultimately achieved, and it is summed up in a short set of equations which prescribe, or predict, all possible patterns of electromagnetic behavior in terms essentially of two leading actors: the electric field, E, and the magnetic field, H, these equations being known as Maxwell's Equations. The remarkable fact is that these electromagnetic equations, which rank with Newton's equations of motion as fundamental cornerstones of physics, remain basically as true and adequate today to describe the electromagnetic phenomena that go on around us as they were when Maxwell finally assembled and put them into shape. If we have a transmission line network to carry megawatts of electric power across the countryside, then we appeal to Maxwell's equations to help us design our system so as to minimize unwanted losses; if in the laboratory we are doing some fundamental experiments at very low temperatures and at high frequencies on metals, then we appeal confidently to Maxwell's equations to tell us how the electric and magnetic fields will penetrate the metal; if we wish to design a new radio telescope to pick up electromagnetic murmurings from outer space, then it is to Maxwell's equations that we turn for designing the antenna and wave guides that will carry the energy from the antenna to our radio receiver, and so on. Little wonder then that willing universal homage is paid to James Clerk Maxwell by all the nations of the world. Maxwell's equations are known as such throughout the English-speaking world.

They are: "Maxwellschegleichungen" to the Germans;
"Les équations de Maxwell" to the French;
"マックスウェル の 方程式" to the Japanese;
and "Уравнение Максвелла" to the Russians.

Such general and comprehensive recognition and agreement about who discovered what is by no means universal. There is a law which tells us that the force acting on an electric charge moving in a magnetic field is directly proportional to the magnitude of the charge, and to its component of velocity perpendicular to the magnetic field; to us this is known as the "Lorentz force," but a French colleague tells me that to him it is "Force de Laplace." In references to the substance of Maxwell's equations no such ambiguity exists; the credit is his alone.[9]

Not only did Maxwell's equations comprise and describe precisely all the known electromagnetic phenomena—and, moreover, electromagnetic behavior under any particular local conditions that one might like to impose—but also when looked at against the backdrop of free, empty space, Maxwell's theory predicted an entirely new phenomenon, that of electromagnetic radiation. This must surely be regarded as the quite unique and crowning achievement of Maxwell's work. And as if this were not enough, Maxwell's electromagnetic theory also introduced firmly into physics the extremely valuable general concept of fields to describe interactions between one body and another.§ Before we go any further with the fruits of Maxwell's theory, let me try now to outline as simply as possible what was involved.

THE CONCEPT OF FIELDS

In everyday life we are well accustomed to pushing and shoving things around us. It seems entirely natural for us to apply forces to objects by placing our hands, feet, or other parts of our body in contact with those objects. Because we learn to do this from the time we are babies, the idea of a force or interaction being transmitted from one body to another "by contact" in this way seems very obvious to us. Indeed, this tendency to seem obvious or trivial is true of everything we do in our normal daily life, and underlies the remark that familiarity breeds contempt. Actually, I am still often amazed myself by the very existence of human beings, and by the puzzle of individual human existence, but I do not believe it troubles most of the human race very

§ Perhaps it would be wise to say that this concept of fields was thus introduced precisely and clearly into *mathematical* physics. Today the realm of physics is really so widespread that one must admit reluctantly that no man can be master of more than a rather small part. So, while many experts, and particularly theoreticians, in nuclear physics would, I presume, agree today that the field concept is of tremendous importance and value, there are other physicists working perhaps in experimental low temperature physics or experimental spectroscopy who might well say that, apart from Maxwell's equations, the concepts of any so-called "field theories" are of little or no direct interest to them. Lest there be any misconception, I must state clearly that I am not a professional theoretician myself and would beg their pardon sincerely if I misrepresent in a rather cavalier fashion (here or elsewhere in this book) either their viewpoint or the significance of rather difficult matters such as field theory.

much from day to day. In short, to most human beings anything that is happening frequently around them must be "natural" or "obvious." (And, incidentally, this outlook very often extends to moral and political problems.) The whole question of contact between material bodies is really not very obvious at all but, because it has confronted us from babyhood, it was long ago elevated to some sort of philosophical principle. (One has to be careful with some of these philosophers; they often feel that by stating something emphatically in words, they have somehow proved that it is inevitable!) And so long as one does not have to worry about any forces or interactions between objects which are *not* in contact with one another, then everything in the garden is lovely.

Newton was one of the first to upset the applecart, and to make men think very seriously about forces between bodies separated by space from one another. In order to explain the motion of the planets around the sun, the motion of the moon around the earth, and to account for gravitational behavior in general, Newton postulated that every material object attracts every other material object with a gravitational force which depends on the mass of both objects, and that this force becomes rapidly stronger the closer the objects are brought together. More precisely, the force is proportional to the product of the masses of the two bodies concerned and to the inverse square of their distance apart. By proposing such a universal force of gravitation at work, Newton could explain very well how the moon was held in its orbit around the earth, and how the earth and the other planets moved in their orbits around the sun. Moreover, in years to follow, the theory proved powerful enough to enable one to predict where *new* planets would be found, from the observed effects disturbing the orbits of those planets that were known already. So far so good. But now we (or rather Newton!) have very definitely raised the problem of a force (the force of universal gravitation) which can operate between bodies even if they are not in contact with one another, or anywhere near it. For example, we have to assume that a force of about one hundred million billion (10^{17}) tons weight is always pulling on the moon across two hundred and forty thousand miles of empty space between the earth and the moon!

In the nineteenth century, the rapidly growing science of electromagnetism offered striking examples of new forces that also could act between bodies which were clearly not in contact with one another. Oersted, as we know, was able to show that a compass needle would be deflected if it was in the neighborhood of a wire carrying a current of electricity, and the subsequent work of Ampère in particular had shown that two wires, each carrying an electric current (but not touching), could attract or repel one another depending on the relative direction of current flow in each wire. As a matter of fact, two homely examples of "action at a distance," as these effects are sometimes called, had been known to human beings for many centuries. If you rub a piece of amber, or some similar substance, it will pick up small bits of paper from the table *before* the amber and the paper are in contact, and you also know very well that a compass needle swings around to point more or less to the north even if you hang it up on a very fine thread so that it is particularly free from any contact with the earth.

Now what is often important when dealing with forces (or for that matter any other problem in science) is to have some adequate "picture," or way of thinking visually about the behavior, to help one in predicting how these forces will act in any given situation. Today this picture usually becomes more valuable the closer one is involved with experimental work, but sometimes the modern theorist is critical of trying to visualize how forces act in nature, and he may say that if we can express the behavior mathematically, then that is the best (and all) that we can do. Faraday's letter of November 13, 1857 to Maxwell (Plate 26) shows clearly that Faraday certainly wished to visualize such forces and interactions, and a favorite and powerful way of so doing is in terms of "lines of (electric) force," which we first mentioned in the previous chapter. One visualizes these lines of force as stretching from an electric charge of one sign to an electric charge of the opposite sign, and so tending to pull them together; similarly one may think of "lines of (magnetic) force" as stretching from one magnetic "pole" of the earth to the other (see again Plate 11a). One can think also of gravitational "lines of force" extending out into space from the earth, for example, so that if something like the moon encounters these lines of force it will tend to be pulled toward the earth by them. Roughly speaking then, one may think of these electric, magnetic, or gravitational lines of force as something like thin rubber fibers under tension, and in fact one can go a very long way in understanding the complicated interaction of various electric charges on one another, by, for example, using just such a model.

If we think of Faraday's discovery of electromagnetic induction where a surge of electric charge was produced whenever the magnet was *moved* in one of Faraday's coils, then we can express this behavior in terms of lines of force by saying that an *electric* force (technically, an *electromotive* force) is produced in a wire or circuit whenever it passes through, or cuts, *magnetic* lines of force. This way of thinking about things can be very appealing and most powerful in suggesting new ideas. After a time these electrical or magnetic lines of force seem to have an existence of their own; and they map out for us a picture of what we call the electric or magnetic "fields." Essentially, this habit of thinking about these lines of force and about electric or magnetic "fields" in space as existing in their own right led Maxwell to his comprehensive electromagnetic theory, and in particular to his remarkable prediction of electromagnetic radiation. The idea of describing *any* type of interaction in physics by some sort of "lines of force," or more generally by some field, is widespread today in theoretical physics, and one who specializes in this sort of thing (which I do not!), is often known as a field theorist. Clearly, his trade owes a great deal to Faraday and Maxwell for the general concepts of field theory. But let us get back to the specific problem of electromagnetism.

THE RELATIONSHIP OF ELECTRICITY AND MAGNETISM

We know that an electric current can produce forces on a magnet in its vicinity, or, in other words, an electric current produces a magnetic "field." Faraday had shown, moreover, that a changing magnetic field (produced either by moving a magnet or by varying an electric current in a coil) could induce an electric current in a neighboring, but separate, coil of wire. Thus, through these fundamental experiments of Oersted, Ampère, and particularly Faraday, various vital facts had been discovered about how electric currents and magnets could interact with one another and, as we have said earlier, these discoveries were already leading to exciting practical developments such as the electric telegraph and the submarine cables. But, in broad terms, what James Clerk Maxwell tried to do was to build up a more *general* picture of these interactions between electric and magnetic effects (or "fields") without worrying so much about actual coils of wire with electric currents in them, or about how in practice one actually produced the magnetic fields. Following Faraday's general lead in concentrating on the "lines of force" or the "fields," Maxwell tried to work out directly and quantitatively the interaction in space of the electric field on the magnetic field, and vice versa, wherever they might exist. In his mind Maxwell invented, or designed, various semi-mechanical models to build up his theory, but in the end he could discard this mental scaffolding and give a complete mathematical description of electromagnetic behavior which holds good to this day.

Consider the production of a magnetic field by a current of electricity in a coil. We know that such a current always involves a movement of electric charge, so from the electrical point of view we may say that something is changing all the time. One of the things Maxwell did was to generalize this discovery boldly, saying in essence: [I] *"A Changing Electric Field Will Always Produce a Magnetic Field."*

But, on the other hand, Faraday had shown that the movement of a magnet could produce an electric current, as we have already seen; so on the same lines this can be generalized to say: [II] *"A Changing Magnetic Field Can Produce an Electric Field."*

The ultimate result of James Clerk Maxwell's work was, in effect, that he expressed these two basic ideas in precise, quantitative terms, and he came out finally with what are now known as *Maxwell's Equations,* which, as I already have said, remain today the standard method of predicting how electricity and magnetism will behave under any given conditions. The acme of Maxwell's work, however, was his discovery that when applied in free, empty space his equations took on a form which is equally descriptive of any undamped wave motion propagating itself freely from place to place. Thus, if you drop a stone into a large pond of water a ripple or wave will proceed out from that place, and some of the energy from the falling stone will radiate outward in the wave from the splash. If you shout to somebody else some distance away, then it is a vibration or wave in the air around you which carries the sound to the distant person; or if you rig up a long, tight rope or string between two points, and then "twang" the rope, you can see a wave running along the rope, and this wave carries some of the energy that you put in the "twang." Again, if there is a violent storm at sea, the energy from this storm gets carried over long distances by waves in the ocean; the waves which smash on the rocks of Newfoundland may well be getting their energy from a storm a thousand miles or more out in the Atlantic Ocean. In each of these latter examples the waves will be damped to some degree or other. For example, waves traveling on the surface of the sea lose some energy by dragging deeper layers of water, by the very fact that water is not entirely free to move by itself, but has a viscosity or "stickiness," which means that the waves ultimately suffer losses by friction.

The particularly remarkable, and unique, feature of *electromagnetic* waves is the fact that they can propagate themselves quite freely without damping through empty space where no matter whatsoever is present, but it is not difficult to see from the two italicized statements above that a self-propelled wave motion of the electromagnetic field might be possible.

Imagine that we have electric and magnetic fields present in a small region of space, and that the fields are changing suitably with time. As the electric field changes at some point in space it will produce a magnetic field in the neighborhood, and if things are right this magnetic field will then reinforce the magnetic field in some regions, and in turn the over-all changing magnetic field will produce again a fresh electric field in its neighborhood. What Maxwell's equations showed was that this process, perhaps somewhat reminiscent of an endless game of leapfrog, could indeed be self-maintained, with the energy constantly radiating outward from where the waves started.

But this was not all. Maxwell was able to predict from this theory, moreover, the *speed* with which such an electromagnetic wave should travel in space. This speed was simply determined by the ratio of two measurements which could be made on electric and magnetic quantities in the laboratory, and it turned out that the speed predicted in this way was very close to the already known speed of light (about 300,000 km/sec $\approx$ 186,000 miles/sec). Furthermore, it is also a well-known characteristic of light that it too can propagate through empty space, as witness the light of day which reaches us unfailingly from the sun across about a hundred million miles of empty space. So Maxwell could finally say with confidence that, physically speaking, light must be a form of electromagnetic radiation.[10]

Some years after Maxwell's death, Heinrich Hertz (1857–94) was able to show experimentally, using electrical apparatus, the direct generation and detection of the electromagnetic waves predicted by Maxwell. These "Hertzian waves" are the great-grandfather of the waves which carry all our radio and television broadcasts today, and in fact radio waves, television waves, light waves, X-rays, and gamma rays, are all members of one and the same family—electromagnetic waves. In free space they all travel with identically the same speed, which for convenience we always refer to as "the velocity of light." What distinguishes one type of wave from another is simply its rate of vibration, or the corresponding wave length (i.e., the distance between two successive "crests" or "troughs" of a wave). A typical radio wave vibrates at, or has a frequency (f) of, about a million times a second ($f = 10^6$ cycles/sec = 1 M c/s), and has a wave length (λ) of about 300 meters. For those who do not mind an equation, the relationship is very simple, namely $f\lambda = c$, where c denotes, as always in physical science, the velocity of light. At the other end of the scale, a gamma ray might have a wave length of only about one ten-billionth part of a centimeter ($\lambda = 10^{-10}$ cm), and a corresponding frequency of vibration of about three hundred billion billion cycles/sec ($f = 3 \times 10^{20}$ c/s).

ELECTROMAGNETIC WAVES

Maxwell's electromagnetic theory also led to intense discussion later about the fundamental nature of the electromagnetic waves involved. Many physicists felt that in order to have a wave at all there had to be "something" to do the waving or vibrating, and they invented a sort of all-pervading, universal, thin soup or consommé which they called the "aether." But whether it is more reasonable to talk about electromagnetic waves in free space (which still worries some people for the same sort of reason that "action at a distance" worried people), or whether it is better to try to think about an all-permeating, vibrating "aether" is not a very burning issue today. What matters now is that Maxwell's Equations are a generally accepted foundation for discussing electromagnetic behavior under the widest range of possible situations, and also that Maxwell's lead in analyzing electromagnetism by means of the electric and magnetic fields has led more generally to the concept of discussing other forms of interaction through some appropriate "field." Indeed, Maxwell himself was at first very inclined to believe that *gravitational* attraction must also be propagated in this way, but he ran up against difficulties with the energy involved which seemed to him then insurmountable.[11]

We have seen that, starting from the picture of "action at a distance" between charges of electricity, Maxwell, following Faraday's lead, could reformulate the problem in terms of a field acting through, and at all points of, space of which the charged particles are, so to speak, now just the "terminals" or "end points." The discovery that this electromagnetic field would vibrate in free space was a great step toward identifying light as an electromagnetic wave, since the wave phenomenon of light (interference, diffraction, etc.) had been known for a long time. At the same time there had always been some persistent reasons for regarding light alternatively as a corpuscular phenomenon, and Einstein was to show, half a century later, that Maxwell's vibrating electromagnetic aether, when coupled with Planck's quantum theory first proposed around 1900, could also then be regarded in a more or less corpuscular manner. What Planck and Einstein showed was that the energy in the electromagnetic field could only exist in certain minimum-sized bundles or "quanta" dependent in magnitude on the frequency of vibration and the newly discovered Planck's constant. These "bundles" of light, or more technically "quanta" of the electromagnetic field, are generally known today as photons. So now we can think of electromagnetic interactions as either conveyed by the vibrating aether or equivalently as conveyed by streams of photons which will to some extent behave like particles. In dealing with many kinds of interactions, including those which hold an atomic nucleus together, modern physics finds it most valuable to be able to think in both these terms without being bound to regard one picture as more necessarily "real" than the other.

THE SPECIAL THEORY OF RELATIVITY AND ITS CONSEQUENCES

The vehement discussions among physicists at the end of the last century about the nature of the electromagnetic, or "luminiferous" aether led in particular to very careful and precise measurements of the velocity of light by Michelson and Morley.** One of the essential features of the Special Theory of Relativity is that the velocity of light in free space turns out to be a very fundamental, and limiting, constant of nature. It was Albert Einstein who finally, in 1905, laid down, clearly and precisely, what was involved in the theory, and one of the most remarkable predictions from this theory was that the observable mass of a body is itself dependent on its velocity, relative to the velocity of light. One consequence of the Special Theory of Relativity is that mass and energy are in a certain sense in-

** Albert Abraham Michelson (1852–1931), 1907 Nobel Prize winner, born in Germany. His parents came to the United States when he was two. Celebrated for his experiments with Edward Williams Morley (1838–1923) on the possible variation of the velocity of light relative to the "aether." Using an extremely ingenious and carefully designed optical interferometer, they were able to determine with high accuracy any possible difference in the velocity of propagation of light in two distinct directions (normally at right angles to one another). This was done at various times of the day and year (so involving the diurnal rotation and annual orbital motion of the earth), but no significant difference could be found in the velocities of propagation. The Michelson-Morley experiment is traditionally regarded as a primary experimental foundation for the Special Theory of Relativity. The Special Theory of Relativity is credited largely to Einstein, but Lorentz, Fitzgerald, and Poincaré also played important parts in its development.

terchangeable. The simplest equation expressing this equivalence of mass (m) and energy (E), namely: $E = mc^2$, is now unhappily notorious, since every film about so-called "atomic energy" and "atomic bombs" usually begins with this equation written in large type against some sinister and melodramatic background. In a wider context, the physical science of our present century has certainly seen some of its greatest developments through the applications of relativity theory, which in turn stems quite directly from Maxwell's electromagnetic theory.

At this very time, 1963, the international situation looks rather black, and it is often tempting for people to be naïve and say: "I wish Einstein had never lived, and then there would be no atom bombs." This is foolish in itself for more than one reason, since in the first place Einstein is no more responsible personally for the discovery of the atom bomb than is William Caxton responsible for all the national and international hatred that is printed in newspapers today. All that science can do is to find out, and understand, more and more about how the physical world around us behaves; what man *does* with this knowledge, politically or commercially, is an entirely different thing, and it is difficult to think of a single invention or discovery that could not be put to misuse just as well as to good purpose. But, if you still wish to blame the atom bomb on Albert Einstein rather than on the general failings of mankind to live peaceably with one another, then you must obviously blame also that very gentle man James Clerk Maxwell, his predecessor Michael Faraday, and so on right back until you come to prehistoric man's first questionings of what went on around him in the world. So if you want to take the view that curiosity about the world is somehow sinful, then I suppose you could quite logically blame all our present worries about atom bombs and so forth on "Original Sin"!

In the end, I am afraid we must all bear responsibility, in one degree or another, for man's misuse of his ability to control nature. If you personally feel that somehow you would like to "blot out" the basic knowledge that enables atomic bombs to exist, then equally well you must be prepared to "blot out" all the rest of scientific knowledge that man has acquired through the centuries, and so run the risk of dying (or living) very painfully because there would be no anesthetics or antibiotics in the world, and no radioactive isotopes to help in curing diseases of one kind and another. You must also be prepared, of course, to do without refrigerators, automobiles, television, radio, washing machines, electric stoves, electric light, and a host of other things without which most people nowadays would find life rather tedious.

The Cavendish Laboratory and Maxwell's Last Days

Maxwell's final task in his quite short life was concerned with the establishment of the Cavendish Laboratory in Cambridge University, and the teaching of physics there. In Plate 27 is reproduced the letter (dated February 13, 1871) inviting Maxwell to put himself forward for the newly established Cavendish Chair of Experimental Physics. It will not be pushing our story ahead unduly to point out that William Thomson's very high reputation is clearly shown in the remarks in the latter part of this letter to Maxwell: "It has, I believe, been ascertained that Sir W. Thomson would not accept the Professorship. I mention this in case you should wish to avoid the possibility of coming into the field against him. . . ." Although Maxwell is usually thought of today as having been a theoretical physicist (and a very great one), it is a fact that he designed and made a considerable amount of apparatus and experimental equipment of his own. The Cavendish Laboratory naturally treasures today its collection of Maxwell's instruments, etc., and a selection is shown in Plates 28 through 31, while in Plate 32 we see a part of a record (in Maxwell's handwriting) of students working on experimental physics at the Cavendish Laboratory in his day.

Maxwell had some digestive symptoms of serious illness as early as two years before his death, but it was in 1879 that he showed disturbing changes. To quote Campbell and Garnett: ". . . his friends at Cambridge . . . missed the elasticity of step, and the well-known sparkle in his eye. During the Easter Term of 1879 he attended the Laboratory daily, but only stayed a very short time." In September 1879 when he was at Glenlair, he became severely ill, and it was decided that in order to be looked after properly he must move either to Edinburgh or Cambridge. Maxwell decided to return to Cambridge, where he arrived on October 8 with his wife. By this time he knew that he was dying of cancer, from which his mother also had died at the same age. His physician in Cambridge, Dr. Paget, tells us:†† "As he had been in health, so was he in sickness and in face of death. The calmness of his mind was never once disturbed. His sufferings were acute for some days after his return to Cambridge, . . . But they were never spoken of by him in a complaining tone. . . . Neither did the approach of death disturb his habitual composure. . . . A few days before his death he asked me [Dr. Paget] how much longer he could last. . . . His only anxiety seemed to be about

†† As quoted by Campbell and Garnett.

his wife, whose health had for a few years been delicate. . . . His intellect also remained clear and apparently unimpaired to the last. . . . No man ever met death more consciously or more calmly. On November 5 he gently passed away."

That Maxwell was a very remarkable human being, as well as a great physicist, is further borne out in a letter from his physician in Scotland, Dr. J. W. Lorraine, to Dr. Paget, dated October 5, 1879:‡‡ ". . . I must say he is one of the best men I have ever met, and a greater merit than his scientific attainments is his being, so far as human judgment can discern, a most perfect example of a Christian gentleman."

It is probably true that, despite his unique achievements, James Clerk Maxwell himself would have appreciated above all a simple tribute of this sort.

NOTES

1. A "dash" or "prime" after a symbol usually denotes mathematical differentiation. It appears that a third physicist, by name Tyndall (but hardly of the same ability as Thomson), was sometimes referred to as "T′′"; this, it has been said, was appropriate to a "quantity of the second order" (or in other words twice removed, or "twice differentiated," from Thomson's brilliance). Tyndall succeeded Faraday at the Royal Institution (see p. 46).

2. In more modern notation this relation reads:

$$\left(\frac{\partial p}{\partial T} \right)_V = \left(\frac{\partial S}{\partial V} \right)_T$$

and this is known as one of "Maxwell's (thermodynamic) relations." In the original notation t was used for temperature, J was Joule's equivalent converting

‡‡ As quoted by Campbell and Garnett.

from work units to heat units, C was a so-called Carnot's function (essentially $1/T$), and M was a coefficient in a differential relation such that:

$$M = T\left(\frac{\partial S}{\partial V}\right)_T$$

3. The relic of this, of course, today is that we *still* talk about such things as "imaginary numbers," although $\sqrt{-1}$ is really no more imaginary or fictitious than is $-2\frac{5}{8}$, or for that matter 0 (which also, I believe, was not admitted as a "respectable" number for a long time).

4. The Universities of Oxford and Cambridge are each made up of a large number of self-governing colleges. The colleges are basically responsible for the care of students (undergraduates) and their preparation for University Examinations. A student must first be accepted by, and must usually reside for at least a year or two in, a college if he wishes to take a degree at these universities. Among the more famous colleges at Cambridge are Trinity, King's, and Caius, and at Oxford, Magdalen, Balliol, and Christ Church.

5. E. J. Routh was born in the same year as Maxwell, 1831, in Quebec City, Canada. He went to school in England and then to Peterhouse, Cambridge, in 1851. After his graduation as Senior Wrangler he was elected a Fellow of his College, and from 1861 to 1882 inclusive the Senior Wrangler at the University was always one of Routh's students. Routh did distinguished work in dynamics, and to him we owe Routh's Rule concerning the moments of inertia of a rigid body. Routh won the Adams Prize at Cambridge in 1877 with his "Essay on the Stability of a Given State of Motion."

6. In Great Britain and the Continent of Europe the title of Professor is usually reserved for the Head of a Department, and the Professor in a Department normally occupies the "Chair" (of Physics, Music, Latin, or

whatever, appropriate to that Department). At least until very recently, the natural ambition of a university lecturer or assistant was therefore to be appointed sooner or later to a Professorship. The increased load of administration, which is one of the curses of our modern society, and the necessity to sit on endless committees, has reduced for many the lure of a Chair.

7. Marischal College was founded in 1593, and King's College, Aberdeen, was founded as early as 1494. All the Scottish universities (St. Andrew's, Glasgow, Edinburgh, and Aberdeen) are quite ancient foundations; St. Andrew's University was founded in 1411. This is in contrast to the so-called "provincial" universities of England; the English universities, apart from Oxford and Cambridge, were all founded within the last two centuries, and most of them within the present century.

8. (Sir) George Gabriel Stokes (1819–1903), mathematician and physicist. Stokes is best known today for his theory of viscosity in fluids. He was President of the Royal Society of London from 1885–92.

9. We should perhaps point out that Maxwell was by no means the *only* physicist who tried to set up a comprehensive theory of electromagnetism during the last century, and certainly others had suspected with reason that there was an intimate connection between light and electrical phenomena. For an authoritative account of the history we refer again to E. T. Whittaker's *History of the Theories of Aether and Electricity;* Alfred O'Rahilly, in his *Electromagnetics* (Longmans, Green & Co., Ltd., and the Cork University Press, 1938) also offers a quite full and critical survey of the various theoretical approaches.

The essential point is that Maxwell did undoubtedly arrive in his characteristic way at his elegant and economical set of equations which are universally accepted today as a remarkably adequate description of electromagnetic phenomena.

10. Let us draw attention again to remarks in the preceding note here (9).

11. In the case of electricity and magnetism, it can be shown that if we think in terms of electric and magnetic fields, then we must suppose that there is an energy associated with every part of space occupied by these fields. So if we start with completely empty space as having zero energy (which, at least in Maxwell's day, was a most reasonable assumption), then the building up of an electromagnetic field will be equivalent to the storage of energy in the "aether." This can all be made quite precise, and very reasonable too, for when the field, once more, is allowed to collapse this stored energy may appear in all sorts of forms—as electric currents and as heat in electric circuits if the collapsing field induces currents, or perhaps as the generation of a radio signal in a distant antenna if the energy is broadcast into space by radiation. But with *gravitation* there is a peculiar difficulty, because in gravitational effects as we know them two pieces of matter always attract one another, and as a result the energy contribution to be associated with a gravitational field in the "aether" must now always be regarded as *negative*.

This dilemma, then, confronted Maxwell: If we start with undisturbed empty space as our zero of energy, how can we make the energy less (i.e., more negative) by introducing gravitational attraction? The difficulty was cogent enough to cause Maxwell to lay aside the question of incorporating gravitational fields into the electromagnetic aether. The general problem continues to hold the interest of experts on the subject, and it is certainly accepted widely today that gravitation must be propagated through space with the same universal velocity, *c*, as that of electromagnetic waves —i.e., "the velocity of light."

It was one of Einstein's dearest aims to produce a unified theory of electromagnetism and gravitation.

Chapter IV

WILLIAM THOMSON—LORD KELVIN

Scientists and Society

Michael Faraday was buried in a modest grave in Highgate Cemetery; James Clerk Maxwell lies in the unpretentious Corsock Churchyard; but William Thomson (Plates 33 and 45), first (and last) Lord Kelvin of Netherhall, near Largs in Scotland, was buried with full honor from his country in Westminster Abbey, London, near to the grave of Sir Isaac Newton. The simple way of Maxwell's passing was allowed in part because the world had not yet realized what an intellectual giant he had been; with Faraday it was presumably his own explicit wish, for throughout his life he was shy of honors, although he received many. We recall that Faraday declined a knighthood from Queen Victoria as Monarch, and he had twice refused the presidency of the Royal Society of London, perhaps the highest honor in science that Britain can offer. But for William Thomson, who lived to the ripe old age of eighty-three, every honor that a scientist might hope for was showered on him, and the whole country seemed to mourn when he died on December 17, 1907. The three men, one feels, were all honest and straightforward individuals, as indeed one would hope to find in people of their mettle, but on the whole I think that William Thomson was probably the least retiring of the three and very likely the easiest of the three for an ordinary human being to get on with. I would guess that he was much delighted by the various honors he received, and that he probably enjoyed everyday life to the full—and perhaps, if one can compare such things among individuals, rather more so than either Faraday or Maxwell did.

If this be so, then perhaps it is no coincidence that if one had to put the three men in some order of greatness, Faraday and Maxwell would come very close to one another, with maybe Maxwell just winning by a "short head," whereas I think it is fair to say that, despite the enormous range of his achievements, Kelvin did not quite attain the intellectual pinnacles that the other two reached. The greatest physicist of all is surely Isaac Newton, and certainly Newton did not seem to find everyday life, or his relations with fellow scientists, particularly easy; and this is well illustrated by the many troubles he ran into over scientific publication. This is not to say that all true geniuses must of necessity be unhappy or troubled men, but probably a certain amount of mental isolation, or mental loneliness, from the rest of the world is almost inevitable if you are singled out by the Fates to be a truly creative person. Yet Albert Einstein presumably would also be regarded by common consent as being on more or less the same plane as Newton, but Einstein did not seem to be particularly troubled or unhappy in his later years. Some three or four years before Einstein died, I had the great privilege of visiting him for advice on a problem, and I would have said then that he was rather a jolly man in person and far from any morbid loneliness or unhappiness. But one must remember that by then Einstein was in his seventies, and he perhaps had been rather less jolly and less at peace with himself in his earlier and most productive years. He once said something to the effect that: "I live in that isolation which is so delicious in old age, and which is such tor-

[33] *Professor William Thomson (later Lord Kelvin)*
when about twenty-eight years of age.

[34] a. (left) Entry to Netherhall Estate near Largs, Scotland, as it is today.
b. (right) Lord Kelvin's mansion-house of Netherhall, as it is today.

[35] Chart showing location of submarine cabling laid across the Atlantic Ocean between Valentia, Ireland, and Heart's Content, Newfoundland, in 1865 and 1866. In front of the chart are two specimens of submarine cables; the smaller piece is from the original cable of 1858 and the larger from the later laying in 1865–66.

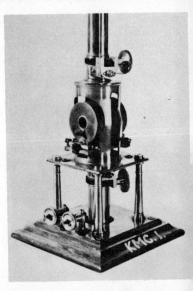

[36] *The "cable" galvanometer used to receive the first transatlantic signals in 1858. From the museum collection of the Natural Philosophy Department at the University of Glasgow.*

[37] *A Kelvin current balance from the Natural Philosophy Department of the University of Glasgow.*

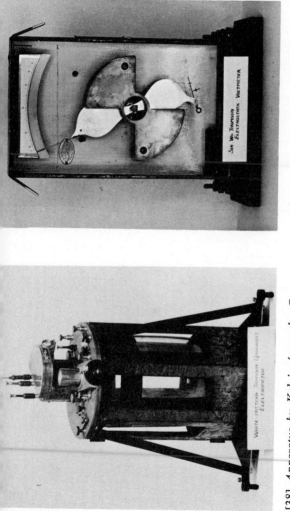

[38] *Apparatus by Kelvin from the Cavendish Laboratory, Cambridge; White-pattern Thomson Quadrant Electrometer.*

[39] *Thomson Electrostatic Voltmeter.*

[40] Letter from William Thomson to Joule. The letter is dated February 15, 1855 and is written from the address "2 College, Glasgow." The letter opens: "My dear Joule—I have just had an apparatus made for illustrating, in my lectures, your discovery that heat is generated by the magnetization or demagnetization of iron, which has proved quite successful...."

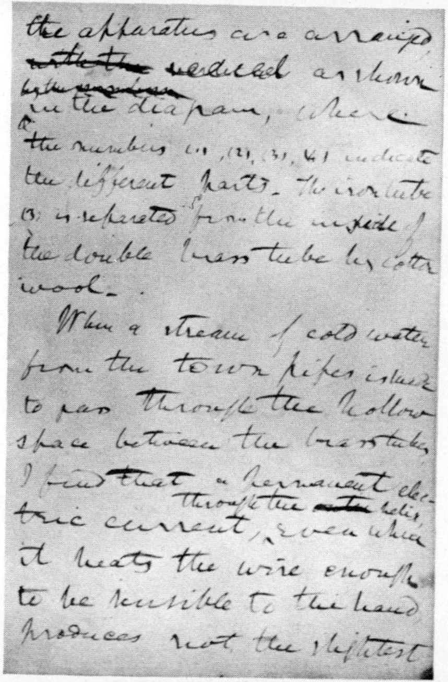

the apparatus are a arrang
reduced as shewn
in the diagram, where the
the reading in 19, 29, 31, 41 indicate
the different parts. The ins lie
as indicated in the middle/
the double lines to be less than
usual.

When a stream of cold water
from the town pipes is made
to pass through the hollow
space between the metals,
I find that a permanent electric current may be
the current, even when
it heats the wire enough
to be sensible to the hand,
produces next the lightest

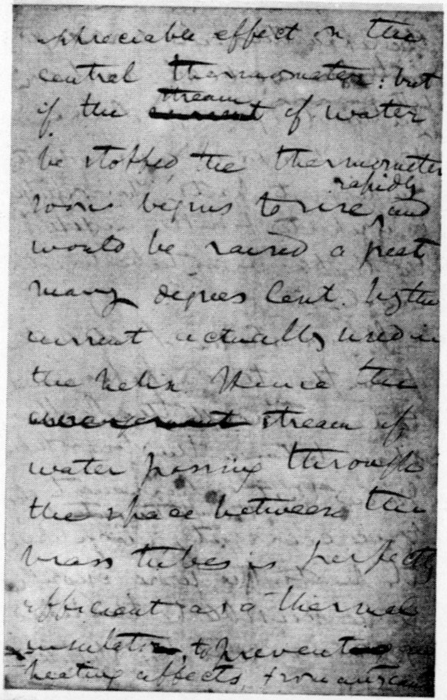

siderable effect in the
actual temperature, but
if the amount of water
be stopped the thermometer
soon begins to rise and
would be raised a heat
many degrees cent. by the
current actually would
the heat which the
movement stream of
water passing through the
space or between the
was to heat it self
heating when the time were

[41] The "new" build-
ings of Glasgow Univer-
sity on Gilmore Hill
overlooking the River
Kelvin. The University
began its move from its
old quarters to this com-
manding new site in
1870.

[42] *Signature of William Thomson dated February 1, 1847 in the Roll Book of the Royal Society of Edinburgh after his election to Fellowship of that Society.*

[43] *Stained glass windows in Westminster Abbey, London, in memory of Lord Kelvin. The inscription reads: "In memory of Baron Kelvin of Largs, Engineer, Natural Philosopher, B: 1824, D: 1907."*

[44] *Stone in Westminster Abbey, London, commemorating burial of William Thomson, Lord Kelvin.*

[45] *Lord Kelvin, Professor of Natural Philosophy at the University of Glasgow from 1846–99; Chancellor of the University of Glasgow, 1904–7. From a portrait in the University of Glasgow by Sir Hubert von Herkomer painted in 1891.*

ture in youth." What I am trying to say is that while I stand in immense awe of all three men—Faraday, Maxwell, and Kelvin—with their great intellects, I am also rather envious of Kelvin in particular, who seems to me perhaps to have had the best of both worlds.

An Auspicious Beginning

William Thomson was born in Belfast, Northern Ireland, on June 26, 1824. The Thomson family hailed originally from Scotland, and by the time William Thomson was seven years old the family had moved from Ireland to Glasgow, in Scotland, where William Thomson's father, James Thomson, had been appointed Professor of Mathematics at Glasgow University (known in the early days as the College of Glasgow). Many people from Northern Ireland have over the years gone to work and settled near Glasgow, so perhaps this, as well as geographic closeness, accounts for some similarity in the local accents of Belfast people and Glasgow folk.

Shortly before James Thomson moved to Glasgow from Ireland, his wife, Margaret, died. William was only six years old, and it seems that thenceforth both William and his older brother, James Thomson, became, and remained, very close in spirit to their father up to his death some sixteen years later. The two sons themselves also remained close friends during their lives, and James Thomson ultimately became Professor of Engineering at Glasgow University, where William Thomson was Professor of Natural Philosophy for almost his entire working life. I mentioned earlier that it is traditional for young men to enter Scottish universities at rather an early age, often around sixteen or seventeen, but it is surely astonishing that William and James Thomson became officially matriculated students at Glasgow University at the ages of ten and twelve, respectively! In fact, William Thomson was attending his father's lectures informally when he was only eight years old; his presence probably infuriated some of the other students, as when some particularly awkward question was puzzling them, William would be heard to pipe up: "Please, papa, please *do* let *me* answer!" With this start in life, it is hardly surprising that his standards were always pretty high for what he felt should be achieved in education. We are told* that he said in the last year of his life: "A boy should have learned by the age of twelve to write his own language with accuracy and some elegance. He should have a reading knowledge of French, should be able to translate Latin and easy Greek authors, and should have some acquaintance with German;—having thus learned the meaning of words the boy should study logic." Since Thomson surely assumed that the requirement of a good working knowledge of elementary mathematics went without saying, our standards of education must have taken rather a hard knock since his time! It is interesting that Thomson himself emphasized the importance of learning the meaning of words. Literature and the sciences should be strongly bound together today by a deep, common desire for accuracy and clarity in what has to be said—but often one looks in vain for a common bond.

After he had spent some time at Glasgow University,

---

* We quote here from an address by Lord Kelvin in 1907 to the Glasgow University Club of London, as recorded in *The Life of William Thomson, Baron Kelvin of Largs* by S. P. Thompson (Macmillan & Co., Ltd., London, 1910). A number of other short quotations which come later, mainly from letters between William Thomson and his father, are taken from S. P. Thompson's book. In future references to this definitive Life of Lord Kelvin we may allude simply to "S. P. Thompson."

it was arranged for William Thomson to enter St. Peter's College (Peterhouse) in the University of Cambridge to specialize in mathematics. He was only seventeen at this time and had already started publishing original work two years earlier. And it speaks well for Professor Kelland of Edinburgh University, whose work had been criticized by Thomson, that he later wrote to Thomson's father saying, ". . . his papers promise to rank your son *soon* amongst the mathematicians of Europe." When we also recall that Clerk Maxwell started publishing original work at the age of fourteen in the *Proceedings of the Royal Society of Edinburgh,* it reminds us very forcibly just how productive and creative a keen young brain can be. Of course, the remarkable genius that these particular men had is very rare, but one wonders whether we fail today to offer the young mind sufficient challenge. It is still quite fashionable to believe that education must be made easy if it is to be acceptable, yet it is rather obvious, one would think, that easy tasks can hardly be challenging.

But in any case, one should not imagine that all this erudition and early intellectual maturity meant that William Thomson was a tedious boy. He and his brother James were well known for their infectious laughter; on one occasion, at a religious service in the Highlands of Scotland, their suppressed giggles got quite out of control and we are told that the minister in his rage leaned down from the pulpit, wagged his finger at the boys, and said: "Ye'll no lauch [laugh] when ye're in hell!" And as a student at Cambridge, William Thomson took part in the many undergraduate activities there, to the extent that his father (who, remember, was a Scot!) had often to write and ask his son to be very careful with money. On one occasion the father wrote: "I think I told you to send me your accounts of expenditure from time to time. Write them on slips of paper on one side, and you can cut them out as occasion may require. Use *all* economy consistent with respectability. . . . You are young: take care you be not led to what is wrong. A false step now, or the acquiring of an improper habit or propensity, might ruin you for life. Frequently look back on your conduct and thence learn wisdom for the future." Again later, when his son was visiting the seaside resort of Cromer, on the east coast of England, to do some quiet studying, Thomson Senior wrote: ". . . You must of course do as others do with regard to expense for lodgings, etc. You may have it in your power, however, . . . to check extravagance in such things, and you ought to do so." The reply which followed must have done little to cheer up the father in his worries about finance: "June 13, 1844. My dear Father, I have again to write to you on the same pleasant business that I had to write to you about so lately, which is to say that my money is again all gone. I spent nearly all the money you sent me in paying my Cambridge bills before I left, . . . so that I have only half a crown left. . . ."

While he was at Cambridge, Thomson became a first-class oarsman, and told his family that he found the exercise helped him to work much better than when he was limited to ". . . walking in the inexpressibly dull country round Cambridge." I am myself inclined to agree that the flat countryside around Cambridge and Oxford would be a poor sort of substitute for the west coast of Scotland generally, and the Firth of Clyde particularly, where Thomson spent many happy holidays with his family and where later his house of Netherhall (Plate 34), near Largs, was to be built. While at Cambridge University, William Thomson also played the French horn and was one of the founders of the Cambridge Musical Society. He may never have been a first-class musician, but at least he always got excited applause in later years from his students at Glasgow University when he himself played the horn in the classroom to illustrate problems in acoustics.

PROFESSOR OF PHYSICS AT GLASGOW UNIVERSITY

Professor James Thomson was most anxious that William should broaden his scientific education by going abroad for some time. So, after graduating at Cambridge, William Thomson spent some months in the laboratories of Victor Regnault in Paris. James Thomson was also most anxious that the youth should always make a good impression at all times at Cambridge and on his own professional colleagues at Glasgow University. Behind this persistent desire was a particular ambition that he cherished for his son. Professor Meikleham, who held the Chair of Natural Philosophy, or Physics, at Glasgow University, was now old and ailing, and James Thomson hoped dearly that his son might in time succeed to this Chair. Before long, Professor Meikleham died at Glasgow, and William Thomson was elected in 1846, at the remarkably young age of twenty-two, to the Chair of Natural Philosophy at Glasgow University. His father was naturally overjoyed but, sadly enough, within two years he died of cholera,[1] which struck Glasgow in 1849. William Thomson devoted his academic life to his work at Glasgow, remaining as Professor of Physics for fifty-three years. In our present day and age, it is sometimes implied that to stay for more than perhaps five years in any one job is to vegetate and be a failure. It is nice to see that William Thomson managed to live a supremely successful and tremendously creative life while remaining in the same job for more than ten times as long. Moreover, the University of Glasgow ultimately bestowed its highest office of Chancellor[2] on Lord Kelvin in 1904, three years before his death.

Despite the long association with Glasgow University, it would be a complete mistake to think of Thomson from the time he accepted the Chair of Physics there as becoming a dreamy, abstracted, and gray-bearded old professor. Early in his working life he was fascinated with the possibilities of electrical currents for signaling over long distances, and before he had been professor in Glasgow for very long, he became personally involved in the company that was trying to lay the first Atlantic cables (Plates 35 and 36). Thomson was only thirty-four when on August 5, 1858, initial success was achieved (although the first cable failed shortly afterwards), and the first message that was ever sent by cable under the Atlantic Ocean was: "Europe and America are united by telegraphic communication! Glory to God in the Highest and on earth peace and good will to all men." Thomson's great part in the success of the cable-laying enterprise was recognized by the Corporation of Glasgow, which made him a Freeman of the city, and a knighthood was also conferred on him; so when he was only thirty-four years old, he became Sir William Thomson.

Thomson throughout his life was in close touch with the world around him, and was ready at all times to spot new and useful techniques that he could use in his laboratory or classroom. When visiting the barber on one occasion, he watched a rubber tube revolving at high speed to operate the hair clippers, and noticed that it showed a remarkable rigidity of shape; immediately he rushed off to get his own instrument maker to make a copy for the classroom. At another time, when he needed a strip of rigid material for some experiment he wanted to do, he immediately asked his (second) wife: "Fanny, have you got a bit of whale-bone about you?" Had Thomson devoted his life to the world of commerce, I think he would certainly have become a tycoon of the highest order. He seems to have had the rather rare faculty of being successful in whatever he chose to put his hand to. Others will have their own favorites among his accomplishments, but to my taste he showed perhaps the greatest perception, and undoubtedly much practical foresight, when in later life he expressed his dislike of motor cars and said that he thought they made people selfish!

Very early in his career Thomson became interested in problems of heat flow. He was only fifteen when his first paper was published, in the *Proceedings of the Cambridge Mathematical Society,* and this paper was related to the mathematical analysis of heat flow. After graduation at Cambridge, Thomson's first move was to spend some months in Regnault's laboratory at the Collège de France in Paris. Regnault was working on problems of thermometry: that is to say, how to establish an objective and universal scale of temperature on which to measure how hot or how cold things are. The understanding of the nature of heat and the establishment of an absolute scale of temperature are cornerstones in the science of thermodynamics to which perhaps William Thomson contributed as much as any other single man. His work in this field is honored by the fact that the absolute scale of temperature, which is used throughout the scientific world today, is measured in "degrees Kelvin." (You will recall that William Thomson ultimately became Lord Kelvin.)

Thomson deduced correctly that there must be a lower limit to how cold anything could become, or, in other words, that there must be an absolute, universal, and natural zero of temperature. In its very simplest terms we may outline the reason as follows. When bodies are hot it means that the atoms have much energy. As far as we know today, there is no universal *upper* limit to this energy, and consequently no universal upper limit to temperature. On the other hand, as we cool bodies down the atoms move less and less, and at the absolute zero of temperature (0°K.) the atoms have the lowest energy possible.† This natural lower limit of temperature is known today as *zero degrees Kelvin* (0°K.), and is equivalent to −273.15°C.; correspondingly the ice point, which determines 0°C., occurs at +273.15°K.

THE FIRST LAW OF THERMODYNAMICS

Now thermodynamics, or the study of heat as a source of power and in its relation to other forms of energy, is a very important part of all physical science, principally because heat is a ubiquitous form of energy in the universe. Indeed, one may say that *all* forms of energy tend to degenerate sooner or later into heat, and we believe that the laws of thermodynamics are among the most general that physical science has to offer. Let me try to outline crudely just why thermodynamics has such an importance in science (and also, oddly enough, in philosophy), and thus why Kelvin's contributions to the science of thermodynamics have been so enduring. In particular, let me try to indicate the broad significance of the First and Second Laws of Thermodynamics.

Think of Niagara Falls for a minute or two. It has been flowing for a very long time, and it is only in fairly recent years that man has used the energy that is available in the water's fall from the top of the Falls to the bottom. It is quite easy to compute how much electrical power can be generated if you know how

† Cf. also, for example, *Near Zero* in the Science Study Series.

much water is flowing each second and how far it has to fall. The conversion of the energy of motion of the water (i.e., the *kinetic energy*) into electrical energy can be done very efficiently by turbines driving electrical generators. If the conversion process could be made 100 per cent efficient, then our output of electrical energy would equal the available kinetic energy of the water, and the balance of energy would be quite exact. But where in turn did the water obtain its kinetic energy? The kinetic energy of the water going over the Falls exists because the level where the water starts its fall from Lake Erie is higher than where it ends in Lake Ontario, and energy deriving from a difference of height, like this, is called *potential energy*. This sort of conversion of energy from one form to another is an example of *conservation of energy,* which is one of the most useful concepts we have in physical science. When a dietician calculates how many calories a man must absorb from his food in order that his body may ultimately perform a certain amount of useful physical work as well as maintain the tissues and keep alive, he is making use of the same principle. The principle of conservation of energy can be summed up simply by saying, "You can't get something for nothing in this world," or perhaps more exactly, "You only get what you pay for."

But now let us return to Niagara Falls. What about all the countless number of years *before* man made any use of the Falls to generate electricity? Surely the water coming from Lake Erie had much the same energy per gallon as it has today; but if so, where did the energy go, which we now reap in the form of electrical energy? Did it just get lost, vanish, or what? Again, if you drive a rather rusty old bicycle, which has not been oiled for years, you will find (if you take the trouble to measure it) that you will have to do a lot more work to get yourself up a given hill, than would strictly be necessary to lift your body and the bicycle from the bottom of the hill to the top. So what has happened to the "lost" energy again this time?

The answer in short is that the seemingly vanished energy has been turned into heat. It was James Prescott Joule (1818–89), with whom Thomson collaborated for some time (Plate 40), whose careful measurements proved finally‡ that heat was indeed just another form of energy, and moreover that the balance in any energy conversion process could always be made exact if one takes into account the heat energy produced.

This then is the essence of the First Law of Thermodynamics, which says that heat itself is one form of energy and that if you take account of all gains and losses of energy (*including* heat) in any physical process, then everything should balance up. But as far as this goes, heat is on the same footing as any other kind of energy —electrical energy, magnetic energy, mechanical energy, or what you will. However, a little experience with the world around us shows that there are some rather definite limitations on heat as a form of *useful* energy. Consider first putting electricity to work. You can use electrical energy from a storage battery or a power line to drive a motor of some sort, and if you are careful enough in minimizing friction and so on, you can convert practically the *whole* of the electrical energy used into some other form of energy such as mechanical work in turning a power drill, or driving a streetcar. In particular, if the hydroelectric company connects its electric power lines to some kind of simple

‡ But we should not forget the remarkable pioneering experiments of Rumford on the boring of cannon (cf. p. 12), which already satisfied Rumford himself that heat was really just energy in another form. It was, however, Joule's work which convinced William Thomson of this principle.

space heater for you, or to the elements on your electric stove, then the whole of the electrical energy they supply is turned into heat directly for you. In fact, 1.17 kilowatt hours (kwh) of electrical power should supply you in this way with exactly 1000 kilocalories of heat every time—no more, no less. But, on the other hand, if one burns some coal, wood, or gasoline in some kind of engine to provide energy in the form of heat, one finds out quite quickly that one can turn only a certain *fraction* of the heat energy into useful work such as driving a steam locomotive or an automobile from place to place. Moreover, this is a very general principle whenever one tries to turn heat energy into work; some of the heat *always* has to be "wasted" by going up the smokestack or out the exhaust of the automobile, and it is this vital difference in status between heat and other forms of energy that led to the Second Law of Thermodynamics.

THE SECOND LAW OF THERMODYNAMICS

The first vital steps in stating the Second Law of Thermodynamics were taken around 1820 by a young French military engineer named Sadi Carnot, who published the now very famous *"Réflexions sur la puissance motrice du feu"* ("Considerations on the motive power of heat"). William Thomson and Emanuel Clausius (1822–88), a very distinguished German physicist, followed up Carnot's lead and firmly established the Second Law of Thermodynamics. The essential foundation is that heat can be turned into useful work only if the heat flows from a higher to a lower temperature, and, moreover, that the larger the difference of temperature the greater the fraction of the heat energy that can be turned into useful work. Now in the hands of Carnot, Kelvin, and Clausius, these apparently quite simple facts about heat led finally to very important conclusions, and formed indeed the basis for the Second Law of Thermodynamics. The First Law recognizes explicitly that heat is simply energy, but the Second Law emphasizes that it is energy of a rather particular kind, and one might say that it is a somewhat "leaky" kind of energy. By this we mean that heat always tends to flow from a hot body to a colder body of its own free will, so to speak, without producing any useful result on the way *unless* one takes particular care to make it do so, such as by using the heat in a steam engine, gasoline motor, or something like that. And, as we have said, the usefulness that one can extract from heat energy depends vitally on how much temperature difference can be provided for the heat to operate through.

KELVIN'S ABSOLUTE SCALE OF TEMPERATURE

The continual tendency for energy in various forms to degenerate into heat, and for the heat itself *always* to leak away from hot to cold, ultimately provides a unique direction in time for natural processes. This "leaky" behavior of heat was expressed quantitatively and precisely by Clausius. He said that the so-called entropy (or the net "disorder" in nature at large) always tends to increase as time goes on if things are left to operate naturally. Clausius summed up neatly the two Laws of Thermodynamics by saying that, while the energy of the universe was constant, the entropy was always on the increase. Furthermore, William Thomson showed how we can define a unique and absolute scale of temperature for all substances in terms of the efficiency of converting heat into work. What is involved is the result, vital in itself, that the optimum fraction of heat energy which one can turn into useful work depends *only* on the temperature difference available to us as measured on Thomson's (Kelvin's) absolute scale of temperature. This result has most important consequences. Thus, it enables one to set an immediate upper limit to the efficiency one can possibly hope for in any engine or process which turns heat energy into useful work, *without* having to know any details whatsoever about the particular process that is going on. The expression for this optimum efficiency (η) of turning heat into work is:

$$\eta = \frac{T_1 - T_2}{T_1}$$

where T_1 is the temperature (on the Kelvin scale) at which the heat is supplied, and T_2 is the temperature at which we can get rid of the unused heat.

So, for example, if we had a very old-fashioned steam engine where the steam was provided at just about the temperature of ordinary boiling water (100°C. $\approx$ 373°K.), and we expel the water vapor finally from the cylinder to the surroundings at, say, 60°C. ($\approx$ 333°K.), then *at the very best* we could only hope for an efficiency of:

$$\eta = \frac{373 - 333}{373} = \frac{40}{373} \approx \frac{1}{10} = 10 \text{ per cent}$$

In other words, at best, we could only convert into useful work about one-tenth of the heat energy we would get by burning fuel, and in fact we could only hope to approach even that meager figure if the engine were mechanically efficient in all other ways (perfectly oiled, no friction in any bearings, etc.). Indeed, we would probably do quite well to get an engine which had an over-all efficiency of 2 per cent or 3 per cent, so it is not astonishing that early steam locomotives were appallingly wasteful of the coal or wood that was shoveled into their furnaces with such gay abandon.

How then could one make a more efficient form of engine using heat energy? If we glance back at the formula for the efficiency, η, we see that this can be done either by raising T_1 or lowering T_2, or, of course, by doing both. Broadly speaking, the internal combustion engine using gasoline or diesel oil is thermodynamically more efficient than a typical steam engine precisely and simply because the fuel is burned at a much higher temperature, and so T_1 is much higher. If, for example, the fuel were burned at 800°C. (≈ 1073°K.), and the exhaust gases released at about 100°C. (≈ 373°K.), then the optimum efficiency possible would be:

$$\eta = \frac{1073 - 373}{1073} = \frac{700}{1073}$$

which is about 65 per cent and obviously a vast improvement over our previous situation. Once again, we could only hope to approach this efficiency if the engine were designed with extreme care for mechanical precision, but presumably a practical efficiency of about 30 or 40 per cent might reasonably be hoped for. If it were also possible to take reasonable steps to cool the exhaust gases further (so reducing T_2), then clearly some additional improvement in efficiency would be expected.

Looking at it the other way round, we can also use this formula for efficiency to tell us what the absolute temperature is on Kelvin's scale if we can conveniently measure the ideal thermodynamic efficiency of some process operating between these temperatures. Thomson's investigations showed that this is most readily done with a gas thermometer. If we arrange to keep constant the volume of gas in a thermometer which is in contact with the temperature to be measured, and we observe the pressure of the gas, then to a good approximation[3] the pressure measured will be directly proportional to the absolute temperature as measured on Kelvin's scale.

The vital importance of Kelvin's absolute scale of temperature is that, although *for convenience* we determine it with a gas thermometer, it applies in principle to *any* physical process that we wish to discuss. Indeed, all fundamental discussions or analyses in physical science today which involve thermal effects are invariably carried out in terms of temperature as measured on the Kelvin absolute scale. The intervals, or *degrees,* on the scale are essentially the same as the familiar *degrees centigrade,* but instead of having the ice point as the arbitrarily chosen zero (0°C.), the Kelvin scale's zero is chosen naturally as the common limit of temperature indicated by appropriately calibrated gas thermometers when the pressure approaches zero. This universal *absolute zero* of temperature comes out experimentally, as we mentioned before, at −273.15°C. In other words, calling this point 0°K., the ice point comes out at +273.15°K. and the temperature of boiling water (100°C.) at 373.15°K. Moreover, if we look back again at our formula for the optimum efficiency of turning heat into work, we see that if we set T_2 as absolute zero (i.e., $T_2 = 0°K.$), then $\eta = 1$ in this limit; in other words, we could then convert heat into work with 100 per cent efficiency, and this offers a sound physical interpretation for this unique absolute zero of temperature. In itself it suggests strongly (as indeed is the case) that one can never go below that limit of temperature, for, if we could do so, η would then exceed unity, which in turn would be impossible. This Kelvin absolute scale of temperature is used almost universally in scientific work today, and its establishment and acceptance is an enviable monument to Thomson's work.

As we have indicated, the fact that heat "on its own" always leaks from hot to cold, and never vice versa, establishes a natural direction of time-flow in the universe; in other words, one might say that heat will flow from hot to cold as naturally and as surely as tomorrow comes after today. If ever you happen to find heat going the opposite way, so that your drink gets hotter and the ice cube gets colder when you put them together in a glass, you had better watch out in case the rest of the world starts going backward in time. The significance of this *irreversibility of time* is of great interest to physicists, chemists, and other scientists, and not only to them. The philosophers over the centuries have pondered time and in our day have also jumped on the bandwagon to try to understand why time in our world always seems to go one way. So philosophers, too, are given to bandying about the Second Law of Thermodynamics when you least expect it! Of course, in the last analysis, birth and death are most irreversible events which affect *everybody,* so the irreversibility of time is really very vital to us all.

THE STUDY OF THERMOELECTRIC RELATIONS

By the age of thirty Thomson had carried out some top-flight work on what is known as thermoelectricity, and this work was quite closely related to thermodynamics. In the early years of the last century, when Oersted and Ampère were making their vital observations relating electric and magnetic effects, the German physicist Thomas Johann Seebeck discovered a fundamental interaction between temperature and electricity. In effect, what he found was that if you connect two different conducting materials together to form a closed electrical circuit (see figure on page 121), and heat one junction of the circuit relative to the other, an electric current will flow round.[4] This flow is a thermoelectric current. If, alternatively, we have an open circuit made up of the two conductors (see figure on page 122) and if we heat one junction, a potential difference will appear across the open terminals of the circuit, and this is often known today as the Seebeck potential. As a general rule, this potential difference grows as the temperature of the hot junction is raised, and the rate of growth of potential difference with temperature is known as the *thermoelectric power,* while the circuit itself is known as a *thermocouple.*

A second effect involving heat and electricity was discovered by Jean Charles Athanase Peltier (1785–1845), which at first sight seems unrelated to the See-beck potential. Peltier found that if you drive an elec-

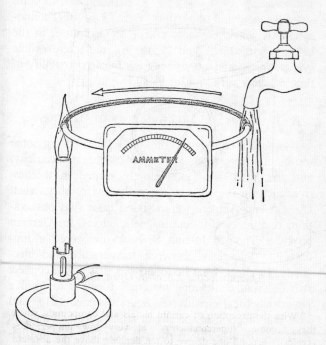

Thermoelectric Effect in Closed Circuit

tric current through the junction of two conductors, then heat may either be given out or absorbed in the junction region, depending on the particular direction of the current flow through the junction. This Peltier heating (or cooling) *at a junction only,* must be distinguished carefully from the much more familiar and inevitable heating which occurs *throughout* all conducting materials§ whenever an electric current is

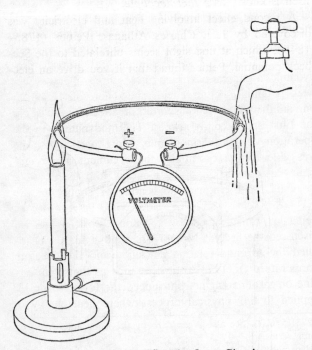

Thermoelectric Effect in Open Circuit

§ With the exception of certain metals and compounds, when they become "superconductors" at very low temperatures (typically around one degree to ten degrees above the absolute zero of temperature; i.e., above zero degrees Kelvin (0°K. or

passed through them, irrespective of the direction of flow. (This universal heating effect is known as Joule heating, after James Prescott Joule. As we mentioned earlier, Joule's work had a considerable influence on the development of William Thomson's thermodynamic ideas.)

William Thomson perceived that in a thermocouple these two effects, the Peltier effect and the thermoelectric current (or Seebeck potential), must be interrelated. After a very detailed theoretical and experimental study he discovered yet a third (and final!) thermoelectric effect, known now as the *Thomson Heat;* moreover, he derived valid relations, based on thermodynamic arguments, linking these three effects (Seebeck potential, Peltier effect, and Thomson Heat) to one another. What Thomson did, in effect, was to apply the First and Second Laws of Thermodynamics to the operation of the thermocouple. More particularly, he was able to use essentially the argument about efficiency of conversion of heat energy into useful work to relate the thermoelectric heating or cooling to the Seebeck potential, since the latter could be regarded as being in principle available for doing work. When we discussed the Second Law of Thermodynamics, we applied the formula relating efficiency and the absolute temperature (p. 117) to devices such as the steam engine or gasoline engine, but indeed the formula can be applied to *any* physical process where heat energy is

---

−273.15°C.). (See also *Near Zero* by the same author in this same series.)

Normally, all electrical conductors have *some* electrical resistance, and hence show Joule heating, but when a metal turns "superconductive" the resistance (to direct current) vanishes *completely;* consequently, if a steady electric current can be started in a ring of such a superconductor, it will continue to flow unchanged so long as the material is kept in the superconducting state.

transformed into some other kind of energy. Thomson's applications of thermodynamics to thermoelectricity not only yielded fundamental physical relations connecting the thermoelectric effects, but continues to be topical today when there is interest in possible practical applications of thermoelectricity in industry. The thermoelectric relations relating Seebeck potential, Peltier effect, and Thomson Heat are known today as the Thomson Relations or Kelvin Relations, and are certainly of the greatest value. For example, by using the Kelvin relations we can derive a knowledge of the Peltier heating or cooling at a junction of two conductors solely from appropriate measurements of the Seebeck potential (more specifically, the thermoelectric power) of a corresponding thermocouple. But it is generally far easier and quicker to measure with accuracy electrical voltages than it is to measure heating and cooling effects directly; so in this way Thomson's Relations can simplify very much our dealings with thermoelectric problems.

Thermocouples have been used for many years as thermometers, but there are two further obvious broad applications for thermoelectricity if reasonable efficiency can be achieved. On the one hand, by utilizing heat which is otherwise wasted (e.g., from factory chimneys, or even from simple heating devices used in houses and so on), we might generate electrical power. On the other hand, by driving an electric current around a suitable thermocouple, we could cool one junction continuously; or in other words thermoelectricity could be used to provide refrigeration (see figures on pages 121 and 122 again). Now, when we are thinking about electrical conductors, it is natural to think mainly of metals which conduct electricity well. But the very fact that metals conduct electricity well means that they also conduct heat rather well, and it is then difficult to maintain a large temperature difference across a thermoelectric generator. But we would expect from the formula for efficiency of converting heat into useful energy (page 117 again) that only by having a reasonably *large* temperature difference $(T_1 - T_2)$ could we hope to have any reasonable efficiency. So what this all means, broadly speaking, is that, if we are limited to using metals, then thermoelectric generators or thermoelectric refrigerators will tend to have very low efficiencies and therefore be of little commercial interest. However, in the last twenty years or so the class of materials known as *semiconductors* has become of great importance (it is from these materials that the immensely popular transitor elements are fabricated). With semiconductors one can adjust the composition and conductive properties of the materials involved over a wide range, and there are then possibilities for producing "custom-made" conductors which can provide thermoelectric generators and refrigerators of promising efficiency. And in all this kind of work we have complete reliance on Kelvin's thermoelectric relations (and indeed on the general laws of thermodynamics, to which he contributed vitally) to help us to analyze and predict the behavior of various thermoelectric materials.

If one is trying to make a commercial refrigerator for domestic use, then certainly the over-all efficiency will be vitally important—after all, not many people would be interested in buying a hundred-dollar refrigerator if it cost a dollar a day to run, in contrast to a more expensive but conventional refrigerator, costing perhaps two cents a day to run. But thermoelectric cooling in principle is extremely simple, requiring no moving parts, refrigerating liquids, or pumps,** and there have been suggestions that cooling by thermoelectric means would therefore be of value in such ticklish problems as neurosurgery on the brain. In that sort of application the net efficiency might well be of little importance, and what might be much *more* important would be the ease and cleanliness in the handling of the instruments, etc., and in these respects a thermoelectric device might score heavily. All in all, thermoelectricity today is much in the news and of great interest in a number of fields, and it would doubtless have gladdened Lord Kelvin's heart to see just how valuable his work has been! (See Plates 37, 38, and 39 for some of Kelvin's instruments.)

THE "ARROW OF TIME"

A great beauty of thermodynamics, to which Kelvin contributed so much, lies in the generality of its conclusions. I indicated earlier that the continual tendency of heat to leak from hot to cold (but never, mark you, in the opposite direction) led in the hands of Clausius and Thomson to what can be called an "Arrow of Time." This in turn leads quite naturally to questions about the age of the universe, and Thomson himself was fascinated by the problem of deducing the age of the earth by studying the rate at which heat now was leaking out from its surface, and trying to determine from this for how long in the past the heat must have been coming out from the center of the earth. On the assumption that the earth started off its career as a rather hot body, the total calculated time of heat leak-

** The reason is that the electricity flowing around the circuit is in effect the refrigerating "liquid," and we "pump" the electricity around by applying a battery or some other source of electric power to the terminals of the circuit.

age to the present would presumably then give a good estimate of what might be called the age of the earth. He was keenly interested in this kind of problem, and within a year of his death he said: "It was this argument that made me think there must have been a beginning. . . . [The atoms] may have all been created as they were, complexity and all, just as they are *now*. But we *know* they have a past. Trace back the past, and one comes to a beginning—to a time zero, beyond which the values are impossible. It's all in Fourier."[5] On this question of the age of the earth Thomson clashed with the geologists and the anthropologists. From his studies of the leakage of heat he estimated that the earth could not be more than about a hundred million years old, while his opponents suggested a figure at least ten times as great. We know today that in this matter Thomson was wrong, because the heat flow argument is complicated by the problem of radioactivity which continually produces heat inside the earth. Thomson can hardly be blamed for this, as radioactivity was not discovered until the end of last century, but I suppose the moral can be drawn that no argument involving the physics of the universe around us can ever be absolutely watertight. It is pleasant to note, however, that one of his opponents in this argument said of him that he had never crossed lances with a "gentler knight."

In his Presidential Address to the British Association Meeting in Edinburgh in 1871, Thomson also discussed the origin of life. He had some difficulty getting into the meeting on that occasion as he forgot his ticket, and the Scottish porter was quite adamant that he could not let him in, saying: "I have nae orders aboot Presidents!" Thomson did get into the meeting finally, and a remark from his speech on that occasion might well sum up the general outlook of science: ". . . Science is bound by the everlasting law of honour to face fearlessly every problem which can fairly be presented to it. If a probable solution, consistent with the ordinary course of nature, can be found, we must not invoke an abnormal act of Creative Power. . . ." (However, I personally cannot share today Thomson's conviction that "overpoweringly strong proofs of intelligent and benevolent design lie all around us. . . ." This basic "law of honour" of science, expressed so clearly by Kelvin, leads people from time to time to characterize science as somehow "immoral." What then sometimes puzzles a scientist is why, if man's brain was "given to him by God" as many would say, he should not use this "God-given" brain to the very limit of its powers. Of course, the general idea that some problems should *never* be tackled, or some questions *never* asked, is very widespread, as witness for example Pandora's box and the common feeling that it is easy to be "too inquisitive for one's own good." I suppose the mark of a really great scientist, or any thinker for that matter, is that he will be driven relentlessly by curiosity about practically anything, whether it is for his own good or not.)

A FULL AND PRODUCTIVE LIFE

One might think that a range of contributions to fundamental science like these we have outlined would be more than enough to satisfy any man; but William Thomson's fertile brain ranged far and wide. We recollect that he received his knighthood, becoming Sir William Thomson, when he was only thirty-four years old, for his part in laying the first Atlantic cable; and it was largely due to Thomson's own great inventive genius in devising sensitive instruments such as special types of galvanometers and recorders to detect tiny electric signals that the whole business worked at all.

But this was not enough to satisfy him in that field of activity. He had to go to sea quite a lot in those days to supervise and inspect the cable-laying operations, and these trips aroused his interest in the problems of navigation at sea. Among instruments he developed were a continuous deep-sea sounding machine and a tide gauge, but certainly his greatest contribution was to make an enormous improvement in the mariner's compass. At that time, a ship's compass was a rather crude affair which was easily affected or even put out of action by the rolling and pitching of the vessel and by the movement of other objects, such as guns, on board the ship. Thomson devised new methods of mounting the compass needle and of compensating for the effect of surrounding objects so as to produce a highly sensitive and very stable instrument; these principles are still, I understand, embodied in naval compasses used to this day. No wonder it was said of William Thomson, "Through him, life has become safer and happier on land and sea alike, continents have been united, and friendships knit closer together"; and a senior naval officer remarked: "Every sailor ought to pray for him every night!" When Queen Victoria bestowed a peerage on Sir William Thomson in 1896, there was some family discussion about the title that he should now adopt. Possibilities such as "Lord Cable" and "Lord Compass" were mooted, although presumably not very seriously; the choice of Lord Kelvin was made after the River Kelvin, on whose banks now stand the buildings of Glasgow University (Plate 41), at which Kelvin had been Professor of Physics for fifty years.

It is obvious that Faraday, Maxwell, and Kelvin all lived exceedingly productive lives, but what I always find staggering about Kelvin's life in particular is the fullness of it in every respect. His pleasure in travel is but one example. Faraday made his one Grand Tour with Davy in Europe, and thereafter one finds no record of any appreciable travel at all. We are told that Maxwell went abroad at least on one occasion to visit Italy (with Mrs. Maxwell in 1867), but it is certainly clear that William Thomson did quite a considerable amount of traveling. His father, Professor James Thomson, took his two sons abroad to Germany when they were quite young; William Thomson worked in Regnault's laboratory in Paris after finishing his degree at Cambridge; and his biographer, S. P. Thompson, tells us: "For the first few years of his professorship Thomson used to repair to Cambridge for the first six or eight weeks of the summer half-year . . . to make acquaintance with the younger men—Steele, Maxwell, and Tait amongst them—who were working at mathematical physics; to row again in an eight-oar boat, or take his old place as second horn in the University orchestra, [which] were attractions not to be resisted. . . . Later in the season he would be preparing for, or attending, the meeting of the British Association. *All of this might be varied with the pleasure of a foreign tour with some selected friend.*"†† He would also spend some of his spare time with his family on holiday on the west coast of Scotland. Thomson's own pleasure in this round of activities is evident, as when he wrote to his sister: "I have the prospect of six months' absolute and unmitigated enjoyment before me. I am looking forward even with greater pleasure to Cambridge than to Switzerland, and so imagine what a pleasant summer I am to have." His propensity for travel continued unabated, and his visits to the continent of Europe were numerous. He visited the United States in 1876 by invitation, to act as a judge at an International Exhibition in Philadelphia organized by the American Government. Again

†† My italics.

in 1884 he attended a meeting of the British Association in Montreal as one of the Section presidents, and also in 1884 delivered a series of lectures at Johns Hopkins University in Baltimore.

Thomson married twice, and although both marriages were childless, I think he enjoyed family life thoroughly. His first marriage was to Margaret Crum in 1852, and Thomson's letters show very clearly how desolate he felt when she died after a rather lengthy illness in 1870, when he was almost forty-six. Perhaps a need for some distraction led him then to buy his yacht, the Lalla Rookh,[6] a substantial vessel of 126 tons, and characteristically he threw himself again into his work unceasingly. Although Thomson had said that he did not expect to find happiness again (presumably, that is, in marriage), he subsequently met Frances Anna Blandy while abroad on a voyage on the Lalla Rookh, and married her at Funchal, Madeira, just before he was fifty.

When Thomson was an undergraduate at Cambridge, you may remember, his father had to write to him quite often about finances, but from the time he was established on his own professionally, William Thomson never seems to have lacked for money. Of course, he had his salary as Professor at Glasgow University, but his patents and consulting fees must have provided a much larger source of income.[7] The Lalla Rookh would cost today at least $100,000, and perhaps twice as much, and we mentioned already the building of his mansion-house, Netherhall, whose cost would be comparable. So undoubtedly William Thomson must have been very comfortably off.

As with Maxwell, Thomson's ability was recognized very early by the Royal Societies of Edinburgh and London; to the former Society he was elected a Fellow when he was only twenty-two years old (Plate 42), and to the latter on June 6, 1851, when he was still only twenty-six. When he was only thirty-one he gave the Bakerian Lecture to the Royal Society of London, dealing with his pioneer work in thermoelectricity, and in the same year he received one of the Royal Medals of that Society. In later life he also received the Copley Medal from the Royal Society of London (which is often regarded as the highest of their awards, apart from the honor of the presidency). The Royal Society of Edinburgh gave him their Keith Medal in 1864, the Gunning Victoria Jubilee Prize in 1887, and elected him President for no less than three different terms of office (1873–78; 1886–90; 1895–1907), and between these last two periods he was elected President of the Royal Society of London for the usual five-year term. After his final retirement as Professor on October 1, 1899, Lord Kelvin continued work on problems which interested him, right up to within a month or two of his death in 1907 at Netherhall. S. P. Thompson tells us that official retirement from the University of Glasgow after fifty-three years' continuous service as Professor affected Kelvin deeply—and very naturally so. On that occasion Kelvin signed the Roll of the University, recording himself as "Research Student."

All in all, in his long, happy, and vastly productive life, Kelvin contributed notably to thermodynamics, electricity and magnetism, elasticity, telegraphy, heat, hydrodynamics, electrical engineering, mathematics, dynamics, and navigation. So it is hardly surprising that for many years he was regarded as the foremost physicist and electrical engineer in the world. Kelvin was invited to take the Chair of Physics when the famous Cavendish Laboratory in Cambridge was founded, but he decided to remain at Glasgow University and turned down the offer in favor of James Clerk Maxwell (see page 96 and Plate 27). A later Cavendish professor, Sir

J. J. Thomson (but by the way, no relation of
Thomson), said of Kelvin: "Modern wireless
phy, telephony and broadcasting depend upon a result
published by him [Lord Kelvin] in 1853."‡‡ Kelvin
died on December 17, 1907, and received the final
honor of burial in Westminster Abbey (Plates 43 and
44).

Despite his widespread contributions to physics, engineering, and science as a whole, Kelvin appears to
have retained throughout his life a remarkable simplicity of character and a full measure of scientific modesty. When he was only twenty-four, he was already
deeply interested in the problems of electricity and
spoke then of its immense possibilities; yet at his Pro-
fessorial Jubilee in Glasgow some forty-eight years
later in 1896, after he had played such a great role in
the whole development of telegraphy and electrical engineering, he said rather wistfully: "I know no more of
electric and magnetic force . . . than I knew and tried
to teach to my students of Natural Philosophy fifty
years ago."

NOTES

1. (Asiatic) cholera showed itself in both Europe and the
   United States in severe epidemics during the last century. The last of these epidemics was in 1873 in the

‡‡ It appears that J. J. Thomson was referring to a paper by
William Thomson entitled "On Transient Electric Currents"
(*Philosophical Magazine,* June 1853). William Thomson in
that paper derived solutions for the behavior of the current in a
damped oscillatory circuit, including in particular the result
that, when the damping is light, the resonant frequency, f_{res},
is given by $2\pi f_{res} = \dfrac{1}{\sqrt{LC}}$, where L is the self-inductance and
C the capacity of the circuit.

United States and in 1866 in the United Kingdom, although it is said that a million deaths from cholera occurred in Russia in 1892.

2. In British universities the standard practice is that the senior man directly responsible for the "day-to-day" running of the university—i.e., the man who is really "in charge"—is called the Vice-Chancellor, or in some universities the Principal (and Vice-Chancellor). Each university has also a Chancellor, who visits the university on special occasions, such as the granting of honorary degrees to particularly distinguished people, and the office of Chancellor itself is essentially an honorary one.

   Today the Chancellor of London University is Queen Elizabeth, the Queen Mother; Winston Churchill is the Chancellor of Bristol University; Prince Philip, the Duke of Edinburgh, is Chancellor of both Edinburgh University and the University of Wales, while Mr. Macmillan, the present Prime Minister of the United Kingdom, is Chancellor of Oxford University.

3. How accurately the pressure is proportional to the absolute temperature depends on how well our gas in the thermometer approaches what is called in the limit an "ideal gas." Gases with light atoms or molecules, such as helium or hydrogen, at normal temperatures and pressures behave very much indeed like "ideal gases."

4. Actually it appears that Seebeck (1770–1831) believed rather that he had observed a direct connection between magnetism and temperature differences. This deduction seems at first quite natural because the flow of electric current in the circuit would of course produce, as Oersted and Ampère showed, a magnetic field surrounding the wire. However, we are also told that Seebeck clung to his thermomagnetic idea rather stubbornly, because it fitted in with some other theories he had; so this is perhaps a useful warning against becoming *too* attached to any particular "pet theory" one may have.

5. Jean Baptiste Joseph Fourier (1768–1830), French mathematician and physicist. Fourier's famous theorem, which he discovered in connection with studies of heat flow, states essentially that any arbitrary curve may be represented to any given accuracy by an appropriate superposition of sinusoidal curves. Oddly enough, Thomson's first paper related to problems of Fourier analysis.

6. The name derives from the title and heroine of a poem by Thomas Moore in 1817. Lalla Rookh was an Indian princess who was on her way to Kashmir to be married; to while away the long journey a young poet recites to her the tales which make up Moore's poem.

7. S. P. Thompson mentions that by the time William Thomson was about fifty years old ". . . for nearly 30 years he had never felt want of money, and for some years past had enjoyed a very large professional income. . . . The partnership of Thomson and Jenkin as consulting engineers . . . brought them each several thousand [pounds] a year." William Thomson himself writes in a letter about ". . . the quadrant electrometer, the mirror galvanometer, and the last recorder patent, which is now bringing £3000 from the Eastern Telegraph Co., £2100 from the Eastern Extension, and £1500 from the Anglo."

INDEX

SCIENCE STUDY SERIES